ACHIEVE LEVEL 3-4

English Revision and Practice

Key Stage 3

Copy the assess[illegible] for reading - Get different types of questions

Marie Lallaway, Tom Johns and Mig Bennett

RISING STARS

Rising Stars UK Ltd, 22 Grafton Street, London W1S 4EX

www.risingstars-uk.com

Published 2008

Editorial: Marieke O'Connor
Illustrations: Phill Burrows
Design: Branford Graphics
Cover design: Words & Pictures Limited

Acknowledgements
p10 National Geographic Kids;
pp11 Extract from *Desert Food Chains* by Richard and Louise Spilsbury (top), Extract from *Little Foxes* by Michael Morpurgo, Egmont (bottom);
p16 Extract from *The Breadwinner* by Leslie Halward;
p17 Extract from *Ramona and Her Mother* by Beverly Cleary;
pp21 HarperCollins Publishers Ltd © 2004, Nigel Slater (top), *When Hitler Stole Pink Rabbit* by Judith Kerr;
p23 Extract from Kiss Kiss "The Landlady" by Roald Dahl. Reproduced by permission of Penguin/Michael Joseph.;
p24 Extract from *Wolf* by Gillian Cross;
pp27 Extract from *Thursday's Child* by Sonya Hartnett (top), Extract from *Neither Here Nor There* by Bill Bryson (bottom);
p29 *Boy* by Roald Dahl. Reproduced by permission of Jonathon Cape Ltd & Penguin Books Ltd.;
p32 Extract from *Love Letters* by Kate Walker;
p34 Extract from *Girls in Love* by Jacqueline Wilson, Doubleday.

Picture acknowledgements
p9 Rob Cousins/Alamy; pp10 Chris Fourie/Dreamstime.com (left), Gjs/Dreamstime.com (right); pp11 Photomyeye/Dreamstime.com (left), Olivier Asselin/Alamy (left top centre), Chode/Dreamstime.com (left middle centre), Mel Gama/Dreamstime.com (right top centre), Marek Kosmal/ Dreamstime.com (right middle centre), Andreea Ardelean/Dreamstime.com (bottom middle), Tzooka/Dreamstime.com (right); p12 iStockphoto; p15 Julian Finney/Getty Images; p19 Simon Grosset/Alamy; p22 Burstein Collection/Corbis; p30 John Peters/Manchester United via Getty Images; pp31 Filipp Bezlutskiy/iStockphoto.com (left, right and bottom middle), Jenny Horne/ iStockphoto.com (top middle); p36 Rod Brouhard; p42 Tony French/Alamy; pp54 Reza/Webistan/Corbis (top left), Ragne Kabanova/Dreamstime.com (top middle), Raycan/Dreamstime.com (top right); A. Arrizurieta/AFP/ Getty Images (bottom).

British Library Cataloguing in Publication Data.
A CIP record for this book is available from the British Library.

ISBN: 978 1 84680 468 7

Printed by Craft Print International Ltd, Singapore

Contents

How to use this book

This book offers you advice about how to improve your reading and writing skills. We know that students **learn by doing** so practice is an important part of the book. It is designed to help you progress towards the next level and do your best in the Key Stage 3 National Tests.

The reading skills section (pages 10–29) and writing skills section (pages 38–57) have the following features to make them easy to use and highlight what you really need to be able to do.

1. **Target level statement** – This tells you what you need to do to move towards the next level in each of the key reading and writing skills. The target level is shown in bold.
2. **Assessment focus** – The main reading or writing skill that is being practised to help you prepare for the National Tests. See pages 6 and 7 for more information.
3. **Tips** – Each page includes tips to remind you of key points that will help you to succeed at a skill.

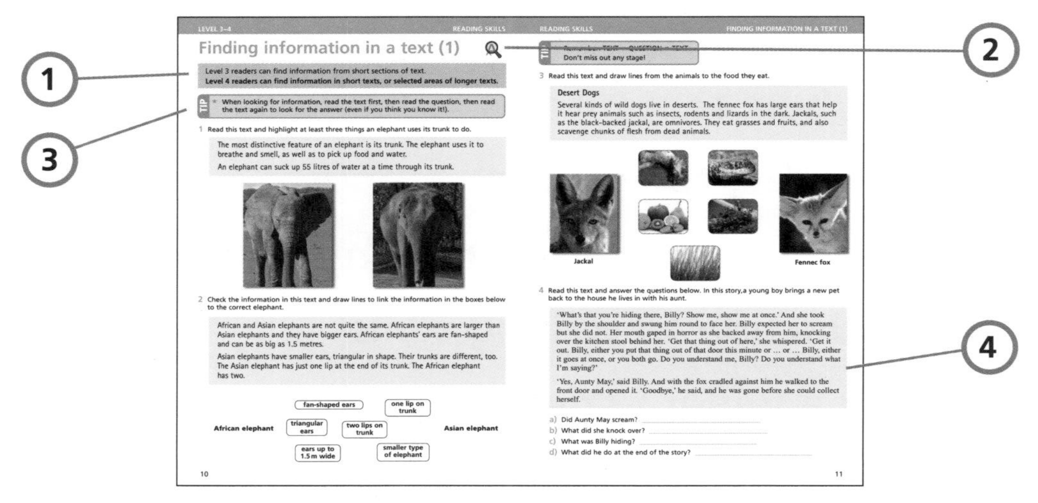

LEVEL 3–4 READING SKILLS

Finding information in a text (1)

Level 3 readers can find information from short sections of text.
Level 4 readers can find information in short texts, or selected areas of longer texts.

TIP
* When looking for information, read the text first, then read the question, then read the text again to look for the answer (even if you think you know it!).

1 Read this text and highlight at least three things an elephant uses its trunk to do.

The most distinctive feature of an elephant is its trunk. The elephant uses it to breathe and smell, as well as to pick up food and water.
An elephant can suck up 55 litres of water at a time through its trunk.

2 Check the information in this text and draw lines to link the information in the boxes below to the correct elephant.

African and Asian elephants are not quite the same. African elephants are larger than Asian elephants and they have bigger ears. African elephants' ears are fan-shaped and can be as big as 1.5 metres.
Asian elephants have smaller ears, triangular in shape. Their trunks are different, too. The Asian elephant has just one lip at the end of its trunk. The African elephant has two.

African elephant | fan-shaped ears | one lip on trunk | triangular ears | two lips on trunk | ears up to 1.5 m wide | smaller type of elephant | **Asian elephant**

10

READING SKILLS FINDING INFORMATION IN A TEXT (1)

TIP
Don't miss out any stage!

3 Read this text and draw lines from the animals to the food they eat.

Desert Dogs
Several kinds of wild dogs live in deserts. The fennec fox has large ears that help it hear prey animals such as insects, rodents and lizards in the dark. Jackals, such as the black-backed jackal, are omnivores. They eat grasses and fruits, and also scavenge chunks of flesh from dead animals.

Jackal
Fennec fox

4 Read this text and answer the questions below. In this story,a young boy brings a new pet back to the house he lives in with his aunt.

'What's that you're hiding there, Billy? Show me, show me at once.' And she took Billy by the shoulder and swung him round to face her. Billy expected her to scream but she did not. Her mouth gaped in horror as she backed away from him, knocking over the kitchen stool behind her. 'Get that thing out of here,' she whispered. 'Get it out. Billy, either you put that thing out of that door this minute or … or … Billy, either it goes at once, or you both go. Do you understand me, Billy? Do you understand what I'm saying?'

'Yes, Aunty May,' said Billy. And with the fox cradled against him he walked to the front door and opened it. 'Goodbye,' he said, and he was gone before she could collect herself.

a) Did Aunty May scream?
b) What did she knock over?
c) What was Billy hiding?
d) What did he do at the end of the story?

11

Example Reading skills page

4. **Text example** – Lots of fiction and non-fiction examples for you to work through.
5. **Practice questions** – Varied exercises help you to practise skills that will help you to improve your reading and writing – both in class and in the National Tests.

   Answers to the practice questions are provided at the back of the book (pages 62–64).

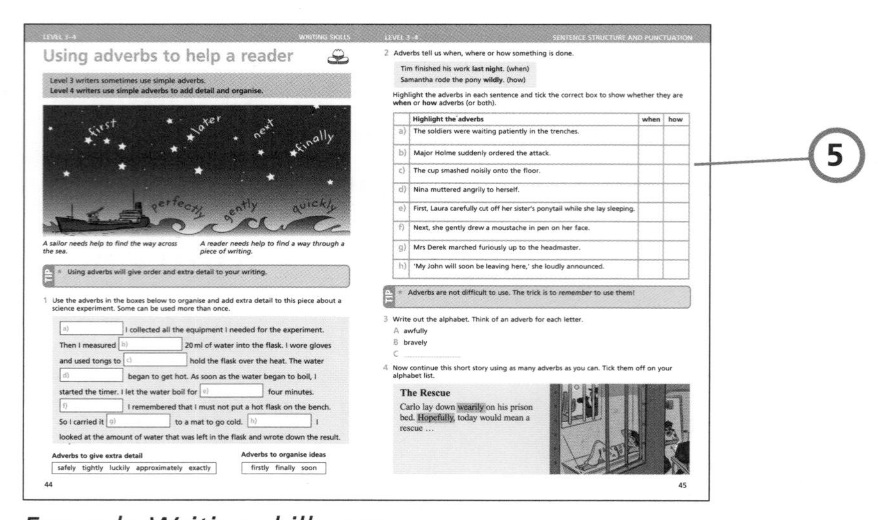

LEVEL 3–4 WRITING SKILLS

Using adverbs to help a reader

Level 3 writers sometimes use simple adverbs.
Level 4 writers use simple adverbs to add detail and organise.

A sailor needs help to find the way across the sea. *A reader needs help to find a way through a piece of writing.*

TIP
* Using adverbs will give order and extra detail to your writing.

1 Use the adverbs in the boxes below to organise and add extra detail to this piece about a science experiment. Some can be used more than once.

a) ____ I collected all the equipment I needed for the experiment. Then I measured b) ____ 20 ml of water into the flask. I wore gloves and used tongs to c) ____ hold the flask over the heat. The water d) ____ began to get hot. As soon as the water began to boil, I started the timer. I let the water boil for e) ____ four minutes. f) ____ I remembered that I must not put a hot flask on the bench. So I carried it g) ____ to a mat to go cold. h) ____ I looked at the amount of water that was left in the flask and wrote down the result.

Adverbs to give extra detail: safely tightly luckily approximately exactly
Adverbs to organise ideas: firstly finally soon

44

LEVEL 3–4 SENTENCE STRUCTURE AND PUNCTUATION

2 Adverbs tell us when, where or how something is done.

Tim finished his work **last night**. (when)
Samantha rode the pony **wildly**. (how)

Highlight the adverbs in each sentence and tick the correct box to show whether they are **when** or **how** adverbs (or both).

	Highlight the adverbs	when	how
a)	The soldiers were waiting patiently in the trenches.		
b)	Major Holme suddenly ordered the attack.		
c)	The cup smashed noisily onto the floor.		
d)	Nina muttered angrily to herself.		
e)	First, Laura carefully cut off her sister's ponytail while she lay sleeping.		
f)	Next, she gently drew a moustache in pen on her face.		
g)	Mrs Derek marched furiously up to the headmaster.		
h)	'My John will soon be leaving here,' she loudly announced.		

TIP
* Adverbs are not difficult to use. The trick is to *remember* to use them!

3 Write out the alphabet. Think of an adverb for each letter.
A awfully
B bravely
C ____

4 Now continue this short story using as many adverbs as you can. Tick them off on your alphabet list.

The Rescue
Carlo lay down wearily on his prison bed. Hopefully, today would mean a rescue …

45

Example Writing skills page

Practice tests

Mini-reading tests (pages 30–37):
Use these tests to practise your reading skills on a longer text extract. The questions are similar in style to those in the National Tests. Each test includes two text extracts and a series of 1, 2 and 3 mark questions. The assessment focus for each question is given to help you identify the key skill you need to answer it. Answers are provided at the end of the book.

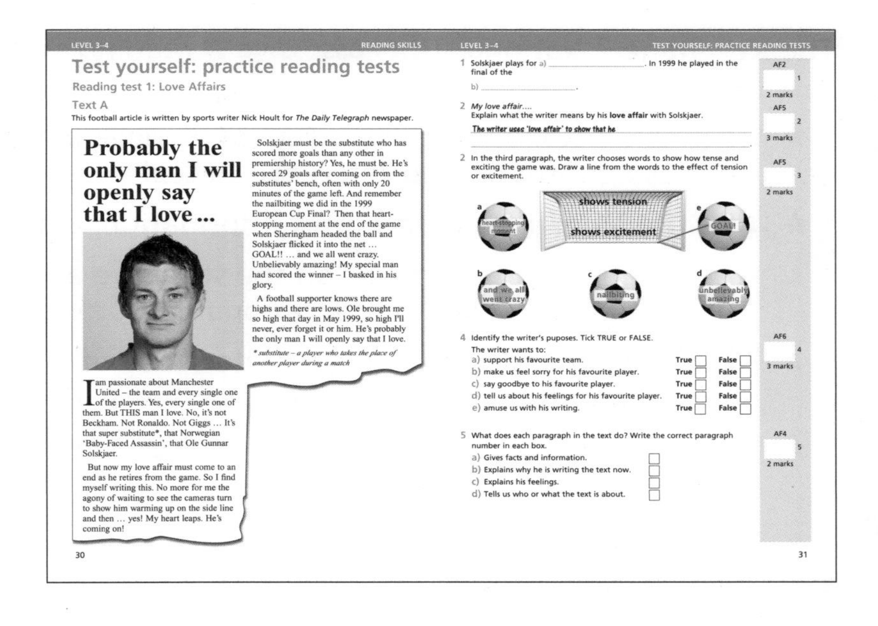
LEVEL 3–4 READING SKILLS

Test yourself: practice reading tests

Reading test 1: Love Affairs

Text A

This football article is written by sports writer Nick Hoult for *The Daily Telegraph* newspaper.

Probably the only man I will openly say that I love ...

I am passionate about Manchester United – the team and every single one of the players. Yes, every single one of them. But THIS man I love. No, it's not Beckham. Not Ronaldo. Not Giggs ... It's that super substitute*, that Norwegian 'Baby-Faced Assassin', that Ole Gunnar Solskjaer.

But now my love affair must come to an end as he retires from the game. So I find myself writing this. No more for me the agony of waiting to see the cameras turn to show him warming up on the side line and then ... yes! My heart leaps. He's coming on!

Solskjaer must be the substitute who has scored more goals than any other in premiership history? Yes, he must be. He's scored 29 goals after coming on from the substitutes' bench, often with only 20 minutes of the game left. And remember the nailbiting we did in the 1999 European Cup Final? Then that heart-stopping moment at the end of the game when Sheringham headed the ball and Solskjaer flicked it into the net ... GOAL!! ... and we all went crazy. Unbelievably amazing! My special man had scored the winner – I basked in his glory.

A football supporter knows there are highs and there are lows. Ole brought me so high that day in May 1999, so high I'll never, ever forget it or him. He's probably the only man I will openly say that I love.

* *substitute – a player who takes the place of another player during a match*

30

LEVEL 3–4 TEST YOURSELF: PRACTICE READING TESTS

1 Solskjaer plays for a) ______. In 1999 he played in the final of the b) ______. (AF2, 1, 2 marks)

2 *My love affair*.... Explain what the writer means by his **love affair** with Solskjaer. The writer uses 'love affair' to show that he ______ (AF5, 2, 3 marks)

3 In the third paragraph, the writer chooses words to show how tense and exciting the game was. Draw a line from the words to the effect of tension or excitement. (AF5, 3, 2 marks)

4 Identify the writer's puposes. Tick TRUE or FALSE. (AF6, 4, 3 marks)
The writer wants to:
a) support his favourite team. True False
b) make us feel sorry for his favourite player. True False
c) say goodbye to his favourite player. True False
d) tell us about his feelings for his favourite player. True False
e) amuse us with his writing. True False

5 What does each paragraph in the text do? Write the correct paragraph number in each box. (AF4, 5, 2 marks)
a) Gives facts and information.
b) Explains why he is writing the text now.
c) Explains his feelings.
d) Tells us who or what the text is about.

31

Writing tasks (pages 59–60):
Use the two National Test-style writing tasks to practise your writing skills on a longer piece of writing. A planning sheet accompanies the longer writing task (page 60). Use it to help you plan your writing and organise your answer before you begin to write it in full.

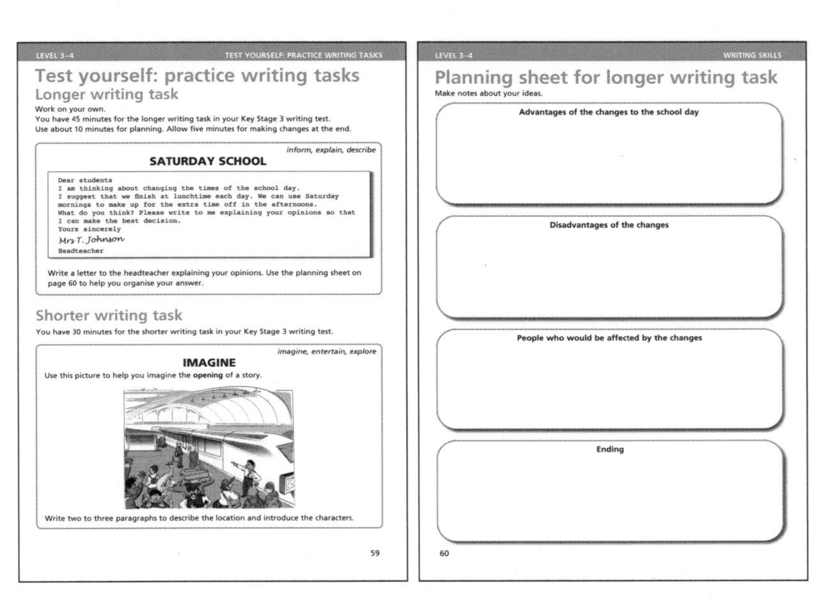
LEVEL 3–4 TEST YOURSELF: PRACTICE WRITING TASKS

Test yourself: practice writing tasks

Longer writing task

Work on your own.
You have 45 minutes for the longer writing task in your Key Stage 3 writing test.
Use about 10 minutes for planning. Allow five minutes for making changes at the end.

inform, explain, describe

SATURDAY SCHOOL

Dear students
I am thinking about changing the times of the school day.
I suggest that we finish at lunchtime each day. We can use Saturday mornings to make up for the extra time off in the afternoons.
What do you think? Please write to me explaining your opinions so that I can make the best decision.
Yours sincerely
Mrs T. Johnson
Headteacher

Write a letter to the headteacher explaining your opinions. Use the planning sheet on page 60 to help you organise your answer.

Shorter writing task

You have 30 minutes for the shorter writing task in your Key Stage 3 writing test.

imagine, entertain, explore

IMAGINE

Use this picture to help you imagine the **opening** of a story.

Write two to three paragraphs to describe the location and introduce the characters.

59

LEVEL 3–4 WRITING SKILLS

Planning sheet for longer writing task

Make notes about your ideas.

Advantages of the changes to the school day

Disadvantages of the changes

People who would be affected by the changes

Ending

60

Writing self-assessment sheet (page 61):
This can be used to identify the level at which you are writing. Find examples in your answer to the shorter and longer writing tasks and highlight them on the grid. When you have highlighted at least 10 of the descriptions for a level it means you have achieved it! Highlight in a different colour the areas you need to improve.

LEVEL 3–4 TEST YOURSELF: PRACTICE WRITING TASKS

Self-assessment sheet

- Look at the descriptions in the Level 4 section of the table.
- In your work, find examples of the descriptions in the table.
- Highlight the description in the table, and an example in your work.
- If you have at least ten of the Level 4 descriptions highlighted, you have achieved Level 4.
- In a different colour, highlight what you still need to improve.

Level	Sentence structure	Punctuation	Paragraph organisation	Organisation inside paragraphs	Effect on the reader
3	I mainly use simple sentences. I mainly use *and* and *but* to connect ideas inside my sentences. I sometimes refer to the different points in time, e.g. past, present.	I use full stops and capital letters. Sometimes I use question marks and exclamation marks. I often use commas to join two sentences, when I should use full stops to separate them. I use some speech punctuation if it is needed.	I sometimes use paragraphs. My paragraphs are written as I think them. They are not in a particular order. I have tried to use an introduction and a conclusion.	The ideas in my paragraphs are not in a particular order. I sometimes use words such as *then* or *and* to add ideas. It can be difficult to see how an idea in one of my paragraphs links to the next one.	I give one idea and then move on to the next idea. I use basic words such as *think, chase, large*. In the longer writing task, I sometimes forget I am writing to the headteacher. In the shorter writing task, I sometimes forget I am writing a story for a reader.
4	I use different lengths and kinds of sentences. I use *because, when* and *if* to connect ideas inside my sentences. I can refer to different points in time, e.g. past, present and future without mistakes.	Most of my sentences have correct full stops or question marks. I use commas for items in a list. I sometimes use commas to separate two parts of a sentence, e.g. *If you go there, you will see* ... When I use speech, my speech marks are mostly correctly placed.	I use paragraphs to group my ideas. My paragraphs are in a logical order, but I haven't made that order clear to my reader. The opening and closing of my writing is clear.	I use a main idea and then add similar ideas to it. I add new ideas to the main idea using *also* or *then*. I use words such as *Next, Secondly, Finally* to make a link with the next paragraph.	I sometimes add detail to an idea by developing it in the next sentence. I use some words which interest my reader such as *suggest, attractive, patient*. In both tasks, I remember who my audience is.

61

Reading skills

The Key Stage 3 National Tests assess your reading skills in the following areas.

- ★ **AF2:** Understand, describe, select or retrieve information, events or ideas from texts and use quotation and reference to text.
- ★ **AF3:** Deduce, infer or interpret information, events or ideas from texts.
- ★ **AF4:** Identify and comment on the structure and organisation of texts, including grammatical and presentational features at text level.
- ★ **AF5:** Explain and comment on writers' use of language, including grammatical and literary features at word and sentence level.
- ★ **AF6:** Identify and comment on writers' purposes and viewpoints and the overall effect of the text on the reader.

Each AF (assessment focus) describes a different set of reading skills.
In this book you will actively revise, practise and improve your ability to do the following.

AF2: Find information in a text (pages 10–13).

AF3: Understand what the writer means but does not tell you directly (pages 14–17).

AF4: Find patterns in a text (pages 18–21).

AF5: Understanding why the writer chooses a word (pages 22–23).
Understanding why writers sometimes use very short sentences (24–25).

AF6: Identify the writer's purpose (pages 26–29).

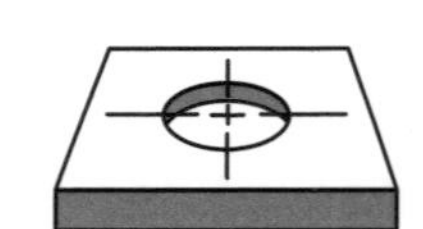

- ✓ Each section targets a different skill and practises the skill in a variety of ways that will help you to develop your understanding of reading in any situation, including for the National Tests.
- ✓ Each section gives you practice at working with both fiction and non-fiction texts. These include examples of print-based and electronic (e.g. Internet) texts.
- ✓ Finally, there are two 'mini' Key Stage 3 National Test-style reading tests for you to check how well your revision is going.

Use the book to work on the skills you know you need to practise. Or, work through the whole book for overall improvement.

Writing skills

The Key Stage 3 National Tests assess your writing skills in the following areas.

In the KS3 National Tests you will be assessed on your ability to do these things.

- ★ **AF1:** Write imaginative, interesting and thoughtful texts.
- ★ **AF2:** Produce texts which are appropriate to task, reader and purpose.
- ★ **AF3:** Organise and present whole texts effectively, sequencing and structuring information, ideas and events.
- ★ **AF4:** Construct paragraphs and use cohesion within and between paragraphs.
- ★ **AF5:** Vary sentences for clarity, purpose and effect.
- ★ **AF6:** Write with technical accuracy of syntax and punctuation in phrases, clauses and sentences.
- ★ **AF7:** Select appropriate and effective vocabulary.

Each assessment focus describes a different feature of writing.

In this book, you will revise, practise and improve your ability to do the following.

AF5/6/7: Construct complex sentences, including use of connectives, adjectives, adverbs and punctuation (pages 40–47).

AF3/4: Organise your writing, focusing on the use of topic sentences (pages 48–49).

AF1/2: Develop ideas, think about the needs of a reader, use interesting vocabulary and a formal style (pages 50–57).

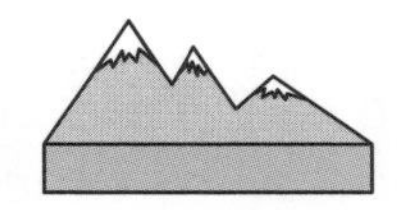

- ✓ At the end of the book there are two National Test-style writing tasks – one shorter and one longer. Use these to practise writing the sort of text you might have to write in your KS3 writing test.
- ✓ Use the self-assessment sheet on page 61 to check what level you are writing at and see what you need to do to improve.
- ✓ Each section targets a different skill and practises that skill in a variety of ways to help you to develop your ability to write in any situation, including for the National Tests.

Use the book to work on the skills you know you need to practise. Or, work through the whole book for overall improvement.

About the Key Stage 3 National Tests in English

You will take three tests in English: the Reading paper, the Shakespeare paper and the Writing paper. These are designed to test your reading and writing skills.

★ **The Reading Test:** This test assesses your reading comprehension. It lasts for 1 hour and 15 minutes. You have the first 15 minutes to read the paper but you cannot open the writing paper until this time is up. You then have 1 hour to answer the questions. Begin by skimming through all the questions. Refer closely to the texts when answering the questions and use evidence from the text to back up questions when you are asked to.

★ **The Writing Test:** There are two writing tasks – one shorter (30 minutes long) and one longer (45 minutes long). Remember to keep your handwriting neat for these tasks to help the examiner mark your paper.

★ **The longer writing task** is a test of extended writing. There is a planning sheet for use with it – use this to make notes and organise your writing. You have 15 minutes' planning time. You must complete this task before starting the shorter writing task. Spelling is not assessed in this task.

★ **The shorter writing task** is a test of your ability to write concisely. Spelling is assessed in this task.

★ **The Shakespeare paper:** This paper is 45 minutes long and includes two extracts from the play you have studied in class. This paper assesses your reading skills, not writing. This book does not cover the Shakespeare paper.

Test techniques

Before the test

1. Revise 'little and often' rather than in long sessions. It is easier to concentrate for a short period of time and you will remember more.
2. Read the tips throughout the book to remind you of important points.
3. Revise with a friend. You can encourage and learn from each other.
4. Be prepared – bring your own pens and pencils with you to the test.

During the test

1. Read the questions carefully, then read them again!
2. Underline key words in the question.
3. If you get stuck, don't stay on the same question – move on! You can come back to it later.
4. Never leave a multiple-choice question unanswered. Make an educated guess if you really can't work out the answer.
5. Check to see how many marks each question is worth. Have you 'earned' those marks with your answer?
6. Check your answers after each question. Does your answer look correct?

Introduction to reading skills

The idea of reading 'skills' may seem an odd idea. After all, you have probably been 'reading' since you were about five years old and can 'read' most of the words you see.

People generally think that 'reading' questions ask you to find information in a text. Some do, but there are other ways in which a person 'reads' a text. Understanding and improving these skills will help you to:

★ get more pleasure from your reading;

★ answer questions in the Key Stage 3 National Tests.

Working with a reading text is a bit like being an archaeologist making a fascinating discovery. You don't see everything at first sight.

Reading skills help you to find the interesting details below the surface of a text.

In this book we focus on developing and practising the following reading skills.

★ Finding information in a text  (pages 10–13)

★ Understanding what the writer means but does not tell you directly  (pages 14–17)

★ Finding patterns in a text  (pages 18–21)

★ Understanding why the writer chooses a word  (pages 22–23)

★ Understanding why writers sometimes use very short sentences  (pages 24–25)

★ Identifying the writer's purpose 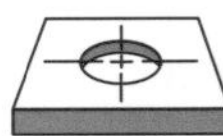 (pages 26–29)

Read the information, do the tasks and check your answers to become a Level 4 reader.

Finding information in a text (1)

Level 3 readers can find information from short sections of text.
Level 4 readers can find information in short texts, or selected areas of longer texts.

TIP ★ When looking for information, read the text first, then read the question, then read the text again to look for the answer (even if you think you know it!).

1 Read this text and highlight at least three things an elephant uses its trunk to do.

The most distinctive feature of an elephant is its trunk. The elephant uses it to breathe and smell, as well as to pick up food and water.

An elephant can suck up 55 litres of water at a time through its trunk.

2 Check the information in this text and draw lines to link the information in the boxes below to the correct elephant.

African and Asian elephants are not quite the same. African elephants are larger than Asian elephants and they have bigger ears. African elephants' ears are fan-shaped and can be as big as 1.5 metres.

Asian elephants have smaller ears, triangular in shape. Their trunks are different, too. The Asian elephant has just one lip at the end of its trunk. The African elephant has two.

African elephant

fan-shaped ears

one lip on trunk

triangular ears

two lips on trunk

ears up to 1.5 m wide

smaller type of elephant

Asian elephant

★ Remember: TEXT ➡ QUESTION ➡ TEXT
Don't miss out any stage!

3 Read this text and draw lines from the animals to the food they eat.

Desert Dogs

Several kinds of wild dogs live in deserts. The fennec fox has large ears that help it hear prey animals such as insects and lizards in the dark. Jackals, such as the black-backed jackal, are omnivores. They eat grasses and fruits, and also scavenge chunks of flesh from dead animals.

Desert Food Chains by Richard and Louise Spilsbury

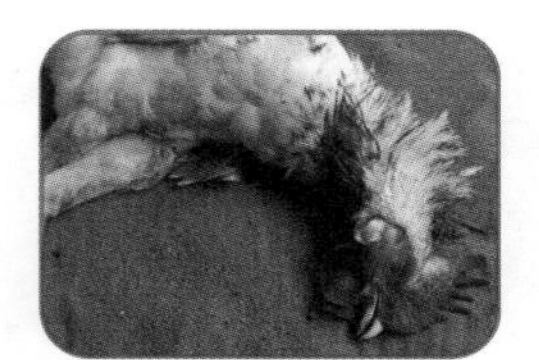

Jackal

Fennec fox

4 Read this text and answer the questions below. In this story, a young boy brings a new pet back to the house he lives in with his aunt.

'What's that you're hiding there, Billy? Show me, show me at once.' And she took Billy by the shoulder and swung him round to face her. Billy expected her to scream but she did not. Her mouth gaped in horror as she backed away from him, knocking over the kitchen stool behind her. 'Get that thing out of here,' she whispered. 'Get it out. Billy, either you put that thing out of that door this minute or … or … Billy, either it goes at once, or you both go. Do you understand me, Billy? Do you understand what I'm saying?'

'Yes, Aunty May,' said Billy. And with the fox cradled against him he walked to the front door and opened it. 'Goodbye,' he said, and he was gone before she could collect herself.

Little Foxes by Michael Morpurgo

a) Did Aunty May scream? ______________________________

b) What did she knock over? ______________________________

c) What was Billy hiding? ______________________________

d) What did he do at the end of the story? ______________________________

Finding information in a text (2)

Level 3 readers can find information from short sections of text.
Level 4 readers can find information in short texts, or selected areas of longer texts.

1 Read this text about pasta and fill in the gaps in the task that follows.

If you are new to cooking, pasta will probably be one of the first things you learn to cook. University students say it is their perfect food – quick to cook and cheap to buy. It is made from just flour, water and salt but some types also contain eggs. Though it is easy to cook you have to get the timing right. Overcooked pasta leads to an unpleasant glue-like meal.

a) ________________ students eat a lot of pasta because it is b) ________________ and c) ________________ . Pasta sometimes contains eggs but usually it is just water, d) ________________ and e) ________________ .

2 Read this menu and answer the questions that follow.

a) Circle these answers on the menu.
  i) What is served with wild rice?
  ii) Which vegetable is steamed?
  iii) What flavour is the pie?

b) Tick the food on the menu that you want to order.
  i) You had curry yesterday and you want a change.
  ii) You don't want broccoli or beans.
  iii) You love chocolate.

★ Identify and highlight key words while you read.

3 Read the script below. Draw lines to match each boy with the type of pizza he ate.

Nick: I went to the pizza place on Sunday with Abdul and Charlie. It was great. Have you been, Tom?
Tom: Yes, I've been there. I had the Three Cheese Pizza.
Nick: I had the Hot and Spicy one. My mate Charlie had it too. You should try it.
Tom: What, me? No, I don't do hot and spicy stuff. I'd rather eat nothing!
Nick: Abdul wouldn't eat it either. He just had plain Cheese and Tomato.

Charlie

Abdul

Tom

Nick

4 Read the news report to find the information. Then fill in the gaps below.

Adverts for foods high in fat, salt and sugar have been banned during television programmes aimed at children under 16, in an effort to tackle obesity levels in children.

But programme makers say the quality of children's programmes will suffer because they will lose an estimated £39 million in advertising income.

Health campaigners had called for a complete ban before the 9 p.m. watershed.

The move is the latest stage in a crackdown on junk food advertising during programmes aimed at, or appealing to, children.

a) The ban is aimed at children aged ________________.

b) The ban is on foods containing a lot of ____________, ____________ and ____________.

c) Programme makers may lose about £____________.

d) Campaigners want to stop the advertising of ____________ before ____________ p.m. at night.

What does the writer mean but not tell you directly? (1)

Level 3 readers can understand some of the writer's simple meanings.
Level 4 readers can understand the writer's meanings, and explain them simply.

TIP ★ In questions, the word 'suggest' means you have to understand what the writer is telling you without actually saying it.

1 In these sentences the writer uses words to *suggest* something about the people in the text. What does the bold phrase suggest? Circle two possible answers for each.

a) Lori gave Josh a **weak smile** and then turned away.

Lori is happy sad angry disappointed.

b) It was hard work walking in that heat with Marco **leaning on her arm** all the time.

Marco is old injured glad unkind.

c) My brother Simon **did a disappearing act** when there were jobs to be done.

Simon is lazy a magician crafty hard-working.

TIP ★ Sometimes you have to look at more than one clue for the right answer.

2 Which answer do *all* the highlighted clues suggest to you? Circle one answer.

a) Mum **banged the plates down** on the table, her **lips tight**, her eyes **narrowed** and her **movements brisk**.

Mum is busy worried angry.

b) Harry's **steps felt light** as he left Marnie at the bus stop. She'd said 'Yes'. She was coming with him to his match tomorrow. He **grinned broadly** and **laughed**.

Harry is pleased about something thinks something is funny is being spiteful.

c) The tiger swished its tail back and forth as it crouched down before him. Its lips curled back slightly from its teeth and its eyes held a steady stare.

The tiger is playful about to attack in pain.

TIP ★ Do not just repeat the words the writer has used. Look for what they *suggest*.

TIP ★ Always make sure you have some 'evidence' for your answers.

3 Read this extract from a teenager's diary. Look for clues to help you do the task below.

Luke's diary

Bad weather so I expected football coaching to be off. But, luckily, it wasn't. Danny was on top form. I'm sure he can't remember all our names because he calls everyone 'dude'. I asked him about it once and he agreed that I was right – but it's funny because he can always remember which football teams we support. Although he is a bit of a nutcase, he is an excellent coach. My game has really improved. But his jokes – they are seriously no good.

Tick whether these are True or False and then highlight the phrases above that helped you to find the True answers. This text *suggests* that ...

a) Luke is pleased to be going to football.	**True** ☐	**False** ☐
b) Luke enjoys Danny's jokes.	**True** ☐	**False** ☐
c) Danny forgets everyone's names.	**True** ☐	**False** ☐
d) Danny is very good at his job.	**True** ☐	**False** ☐

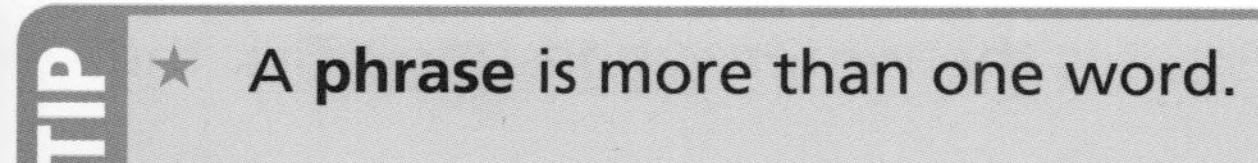

TIP ★ A **phrase** is more than one word.

4 Read this text about a tennis player and answer the questions below.

http://www.

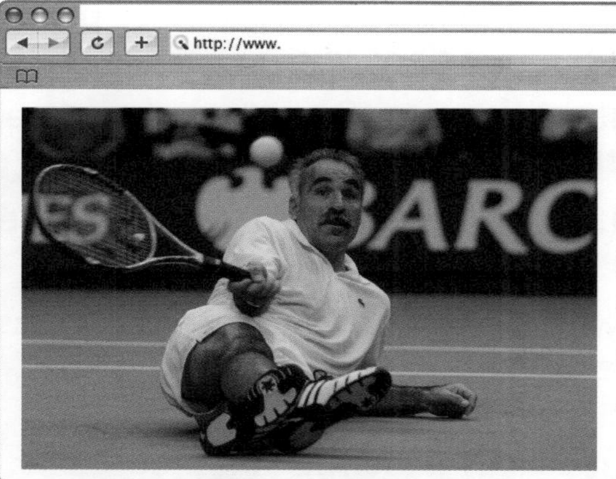

Mansour Bahrami is the most entertaining tennis player of all time – the joker of the tennis world. His skilful trick shots have the crowd applauding and cheering. Serving with six balls in his hand, playing whilst sitting in a chair, play-acting with his doubles partner and pretending to have arguments with his opponents are only a few of his antics ...

Tennis is never dull when the clown prince takes to the court.

a) Find three **words** that *suggest* people like to watch Bahrami play tennis.

______________ ______________ ______________

b) Find two **phrases** used to describe Bahrami that *suggest* he is funny.

____

____

What does the writer mean but not tell you directly? (2)

Level 3 readers can understand some of the writer's simple meanings.
Level 4 readers can understand the writer's meanings, and explain them simply.

1 Read this short text. The writer of this piece gives an impression, rather than saying something directly. Find the correct words or phrases and write them in the table.

We piled out of the bus, charged up the steps and beamed at Mum as she opened the door. The holiday was over at last.

The writer wants you to know that ...	Which word or phrase suggests this?
a) the children were hurrying	
b) the children were pleased	
c) the holiday had not been good	

TIP ★ Do not just repeat the words the writer has used. Look for what they *suggest*.

2 Read this text from a leaflet about a theme park. What is the writer suggesting? Tick the correct answer.

First things first, remember it's a whole day! Not a couple of hours or a few minutes. You have an entire day to enjoy the mass of magical entertainment ahead of you.

- ☐ A day is not enough time to do everything.
- ☐ Don't rush because you have plenty of time in a day's visit.
- ☐ It only takes a few minutes to do each thing.
- ☐ It is the best day you will ever have.

3 Read this extract from a story about a boy in trouble with his father. Highlight the **phrase** which *suggests* that the father is behaving like a fierce animal.

The father advanced on the boy, his teeth showing in a snarl under his big moustache.
'Where's the money?' he almost whispered.
'I lost it,' he said.
'You – what?' cried the father.
'I lost it,' the boy repeated.
The man began to shout and wave his hands about.
'Lost it! Lost it! What are you talking about? How could you lose it?'

The Breadwinner by Leslie Halward

TIP ★ A **phrase** is more than one word and less than a full sentence, e.g. *The man began to shout and wave his hands about.*

4 Read this story and answer the questions below. A young girl called Ramona tells her parents and brother she is going to run away.

> Ramona made up her mind to shock her parents, really shock them.
>
> 'I am going to run away,' she announced.
>
> 'I'm sorry to hear that,' said Mr Quimby.
>
> 'When are you leaving?' enquired Ramona's mother politely.
>
> The question was almost more than Ramona could bear. Her mother was supposed to say, Oh Ramona, please, please don't leave me!
>
> 'Today,' Ramona managed to say with quivering lips. 'This morning.'
>
> 'She just wants you to feel sorry for her,' said heartless Beezus. 'She wants you to stop her.'
>
> Ramona waited for her mother or father to say something, but neither spoke. Finally there was nothing for Ramona to do but get up from the couch. 'I guess I'll go pack,' she said, and started towards her room.
>
> *Ramona and Her Mother* by Beverly Cleary

a) Circle the correct phrase to fill the gap.

The writer suggests that Ramona ______________________ to run away.

is determined **is happy** **doesn't really want** **is desperate**

b) Highlight clues in the text that explain *why* you think this.

c) The writer suggests that Ramona's parents are ______________________ .

cruel to her **shocked by her** **used to her** **worried about her**

d) Highlight clues in the text that explain *why* you think this.

e) Highlight two **phrases** in the text that suggest that Ramona is very upset.

f) The word ______________________ suggests Beezus doesn't care about Ramona's feelings.

TIP ★ You will generally need to use your own words to explain what the text suggests to you.

5 Write an instruction to tell your friend how to find out what the writer is suggesting in a text, e.g. Look for … and … that give you … .

____

____

____

Finding patterns in a text (1)

Level 3 readers can identify some simple features of text organisation.
Level 4 readers can identify the basic overall organisation of a text.

Writers *choose* the overall pattern of their work to have the best effect on a reader.

1 The writer of this horoscope has used colour to organise the text. Fill in the boxes with these labels:

love life   title   action   sub-title

Aquarius Jan 20–Feb 18

Life: You are trying too hard – just be yourself and people will love you as you are.

Love: Bored with the usual boys? Try looking in places you never thought to look.

Friends: Plan a girls' night – invite your best friends over for a girlie DVD, then get out the make-up and transform yourselves into the stars.

Capricorn Dec 22–Jan 19

Life: You will have to let others win this month – you can't always have it your own way.

Love: Look out! The guy for you might be someone you already know.

Friends: Do something positive! Raise money for a charity, organise a party – get out there!

a

b

c

d

2 Write the next horoscope for Libra (September 23–October 22) following the same pattern as you have found in the ones above.

3 Read this text. Describe what happens in each section by matching the labels and drawing lines to the right section. One has been done for you.

offers hope

gives a promise

asks for money

Goodbye, Loyal Little Donkey?

Day after day, this little donkey had to march miles along busy, dangerous roads so his owner could feed his family. Carrying a heavy load, it was only a matter of time before he stumbled and fell.

Without our organisation, horses and donkeys around the world would be left to die by the roadside. Now we desperately need your help to pay for the cost of our mobile animal hospitals – bringing urgent help to suffering animals.

£25 COULD PAY FOR EMERGENCY TREATMENTS FOR 50 ANIMALS.

Your gift will be spent treating working horses and donkeys, where the need is greatest.

describes suffering

quickly catches reader's attention

TIP ★ Looking at the 'job' of each section helps you to understand the organisation of a text.

4 Find a leaflet of your own. Identify the 'job' of each section.

Finding patterns in a text (2)

Level 3 readers can identify some simple features of text organisation.
Level 4 readers can identify the basic overall organisation of a text.

TIP
★ If the writing focuses on one thing and then moves to another, the writer *chooses* to organise it this way. Look out for any **changes** in the text. Think about why they happen.

1 These two texts describe going to a theme park. Which description do you like the best?

Tom

Kirsty

2 Show how each description is organised by filling in the gaps.

a) Tom's description:

First of all, he describes ______________________________. Then he tells you

______________________________.

b) Kirsty's description:

First of all, she describes ______________________________. Then she tells you

______________________________.

c) I prefer ______________'s description because ______________________________.

3 a) Write a three-sentence account of a disastrous event giving the ending first.

____

____

____

b) Write about the same event but give the ending last.

____

____

____

4 Read this description of a painful event and answer the questions.

One day my father came home from work, and even before he had taken off his coat he grabbed one of our jam tarts from the wire cooling rack. He couldn't have known they had come from the oven only a minute or two before. His hands flapped, his face turned a deep raspberry red, beads of sweat formed like warts on his brow, he danced a merry dance. As he tried to swallow and his eyes filled with the sort of tears a man can only summon when he has boiling lemon curd stuck to the roof of his mouth, I am sure that I saw the faintest of smiles flicker across my mother's face.

Toast by Nigel Slater

a) Who is the writer concentrating on for most of the text?

b) Who is the writer concentrating on at the end?

c) Why has the writer *chosen* to change the person he is concentrating on?

TIP ★ In a text about characters, look out for changes in the character that the writer is concentrating on.

5 Read this extract from a story about Mama, Max and Anna. They are trying to escape on a train during the Second World War. The passport inspector comes to their compartment.

He looked at the passport of the lady with the basket, nodded, stamped it with a little rubber stamp, and gave it back to her.

Then he turned to Mama. Mama handed him the passports and smiled. But the hand with which she was holding her handbag was squeezing it into terrible contortions. The man examined the passports. Then he looked at Mama to see if it was the same face as on the passport photograph, then at Max and then at Anna. Then he got out his rubber stamp. Then he remembered something and looked at the passports again. Then at last he stamped them and gave them back to Mama.

'Pleasant journey,' he said as he opened the door of the compartment.

When Hitler Stole Pink Rabbit by Judith Kerr

a) Most of this text focuses on the passport inspector but some of it focuses on Mama. Highlight the sentences which focus on Mama.

b) Read the text without the sentences focusing on Mama. Now, explain why the writer chose to put those sentences in the middle of this section.

TIP ★ The person the writer concentrates on is the **focus** of attention, like a camera lens **focuses** on a particular object.

Understanding why the writer chooses a word

Level 3 readers can identify simple language features.
Level 4 readers can identify interesting language and make simple comments about it.

1 Choose some words to help you to describe this picture.

painful

2 Read this short paragraph about a man on a train. Put the red words and phrases into three groups in the table below to show how they help to build up an impression of the man.

The man in the seat opposite to me had a **button nose** and **small, piggy eyes**. He was **well-dressed** in a **smart pin-stripe suit** but his tie was **frayed** and **stained**. The newspaper he had opened at the start of the journey was **still unread**, as he kept looking around him **anxiously**, as if expecting someone else to arrive.

Positive impression	Negative impression	Neutral impression

TIP
★ *Similar ... but different ...*
Words can be quite similar, but their effect is different. You need to begin to recognise differences between words.

3 Explain the difference between the following pairs of words.
a) BULLYING and BOSSY
b) HOUSE and HOME

★ Writers *choose* each word they use. They *choose* the word so that it has a particular *effect* on the reader. The word will suggest ideas to the reader.

Think about what the word *suggests* to you as well as what it **means**.

4 What creature, person and natural power do you associate with the words in the table below? Fill in the table following the examples given.

Word	Animal	Person	Natural power
roar	lion	army sergeant shouting at troops	waves crashing into a cave on the seashore
thunder			
bark			
whine			

5 This is the beginning of a Roald Dahl story, *The Landlady*. A young man arrives in a new town. Read the extract and answer the questions.

> Billy Weaver had travelled down from London on the slow afternoon train with a change at Swindon on the way, and by the time he got to Bath it was about 9 o'clock in the evening and the moon was coming up out of a clear starry sky over the houses opposite the station entrance. But the air was deadly cold and the wind was like a flat blade of ice on his cheeks.

a) The writer could have used 'very cold' instead of 'deadly cold'. 'Deadly' is a better choice because it suggests ______________________________.

b) The writer could have used 'the wind was like ice'. 'Like a flat blade of ice' is better because it suggests ______________________________.

Understanding why writers sometimes use very short sentences

Level 3 readers can identify simple language features.

Level 4 readers can identify interesting language and make simple comments about it.

Writers make lots of choices. The length of a sentence can have an effect on the reader, so writers sometimes choose to use short sentences. Short sentences never appear by accident. They always have a job to do.

1 Read this story, in which Cassy's father comes home, bringing some problems to the family. Then do the exercises that follow.

> He came in the early morning, at about half past two. His feet padded along the balcony, slinking silently past the closed doors of the other flats. No one glimpsed his shadow, flickering across the curtain or noticed the uneven rhythm of his steps.
>
> But he woke Cassy. She lay in her bed under the window and listened as the footsteps stopped outside. There were two quick, light taps ... like a signal.
>
> Cassy sat up slowly. She heard the door of the back room open and Nan come hurrying out.
>
> *Wolf* by Gillian Cross

a) Highlight the two short sentences.

b) The writer uses short sentences to draw the reader's attention to

Cassy **her father** **Nan.**

Circle the correct answer.

2 Read this extract, in which Simon deals with his anger. Do the exercises that follow.

a) [ ]

Simon had had enough this time. Enough really did mean enough.

He began by carefully tearing the pages from the open book on his desk. Next he opened up a wardrobe and pulled trousers, jumpers, t-shirts onto the floor. He ripped posters from the walls. He kicked over his lamp. He smashed the mirror. He shouted. He cried. He collapsed.

b) [ ]

c) [ ]

The short sentences in this story have different 'jobs'. Copy the correct label given here into the three boxes around the text.

bring the action to a close	emphasise a feeling	speed up the action

TIP ★ When you think you know *why* a short sentence is used, check that your idea fits in with the story.

3 Read this extract, in which two boy detectives find themselves in an unwanted fight.

The question hung in the air like a DVD on pause. The two friends looked at each other in horror. In a flash, they realised the terrible trap they had fallen into.

With only a moment's hesitation, Ashley threw himself like a battering ram against the first man. The second man raised his gun, but Finlay was too quick. Picking up a brick, he bashed it against the man's hand as hard as he could. Bones cracked.

Punches flew wildly, sending them all off balance and spilling off the pavement into the road. Cars swerved. Horns sounded. A bus glanced past. Fighting back was no longer on the minds of the two boys as they just tried to survive the traffic.

a) Highlight the short sentences.

b) Complete the sentences below to show what 'jobs' the short sentences are doing.

i) The writer uses the first short sentence to ______________________

____.

ii) The second group of short sentences is used to ______________________

____.

Identifying the writer's purpose (1) 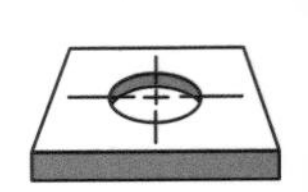

Level 3 readers can identify the main purpose of a text.
Level 4 readers can identify and make simple comments about the purpose of a text.

When you speak to people, you have an effect on them.

It is the same with writing. Writers will think about the effect they want to have on the reader and then *choose* information and words to achieve this effect.

TIP
★ Imagine how the writer would read the words to you. What kind of voice would they use?

1 Read these short texts. What effect does the writer want to have on the reader? Choose from the words or phrases below. There may be more than one correct answer!

a) The news is not good. We wait in hope … Join me tomorrow at 8.

b) If you want to join the Ambulance Service, you'll need five GCSEs and four years' driving experience.

c) If you are visiting Bahrain, stay at The Al Dana Resort Hotel with its private beach and heated outdoor pool. Try its famous international restaurant and then relax in its marble lounges.

d) He's new on the comedy circuit but, as far as I'm concerned, he has nothing new to amuse us.

inform	describe character	advise
persuade	amuse	
create suspense	give an opinion	

2 Read this story in which a girl has just seen her brother disappear under a mud slide. Then answer the questions that follow.

> I pounced through the creek to where he'd been standing and started scrabbling at the dirt, yelling out his name. The earth was heavy and sticky: my fingers left slick gouges behind them but hardly took anything away. I screeched to him over and over, thinking that if he could hear me he'd be comforted, all the while thrashing at the mud, spattering it into my hair and eyes and spitting it out with my cries.
>
> *Thursday's Child* by Sonya Hartnett

a) What is the writer trying to do in this text? Circle one of these phrases.

describe a character **create tension** **give an opinion**

b) What clues are there in the text to tell you that this is the writer's purpose?

____

3 Read this text, in which the writer focuses on car parking in Rome.

> I love the way the Italians park. You turn any street corner in Rome and it looks as if you've just missed a parking competition for blind people. Cars are pointed in every direction, half on the pavements and half off, facing in, facing sideways, blocking garages and side streets and phone boxes, fitted into spaces so tight that the only possible way out would be through the sun roof.

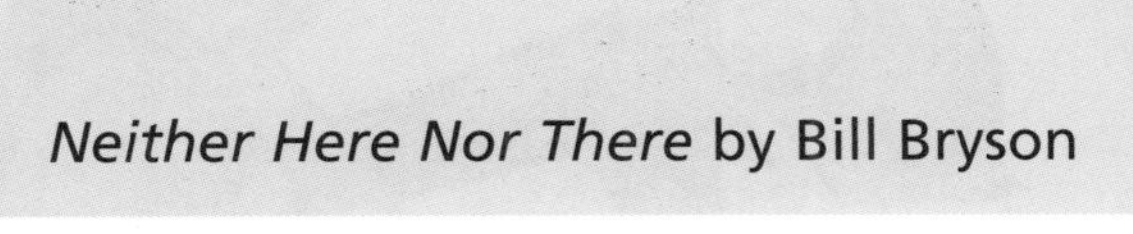

> *Neither Here Nor There* by Bill Bryson

a) What is the writer trying to do in this text? Circle one of these phrases.

advise **entertain** **give information** **give an opinion**

b) What clues are there in the text to tell you that this is the writer's purpose?

____

Identifying the writer's purpose (2)

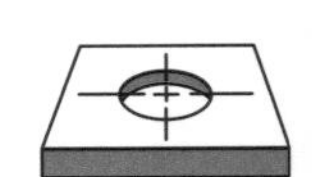

Level 3 readers can identify the main purpose of a text.
Level 4 readers can identify and make simple comments about the purpose of a text.

1 Find the pairs of speech bubbles with the same purpose and draw a line to link them with the purpose in the centre. One has been done for you.

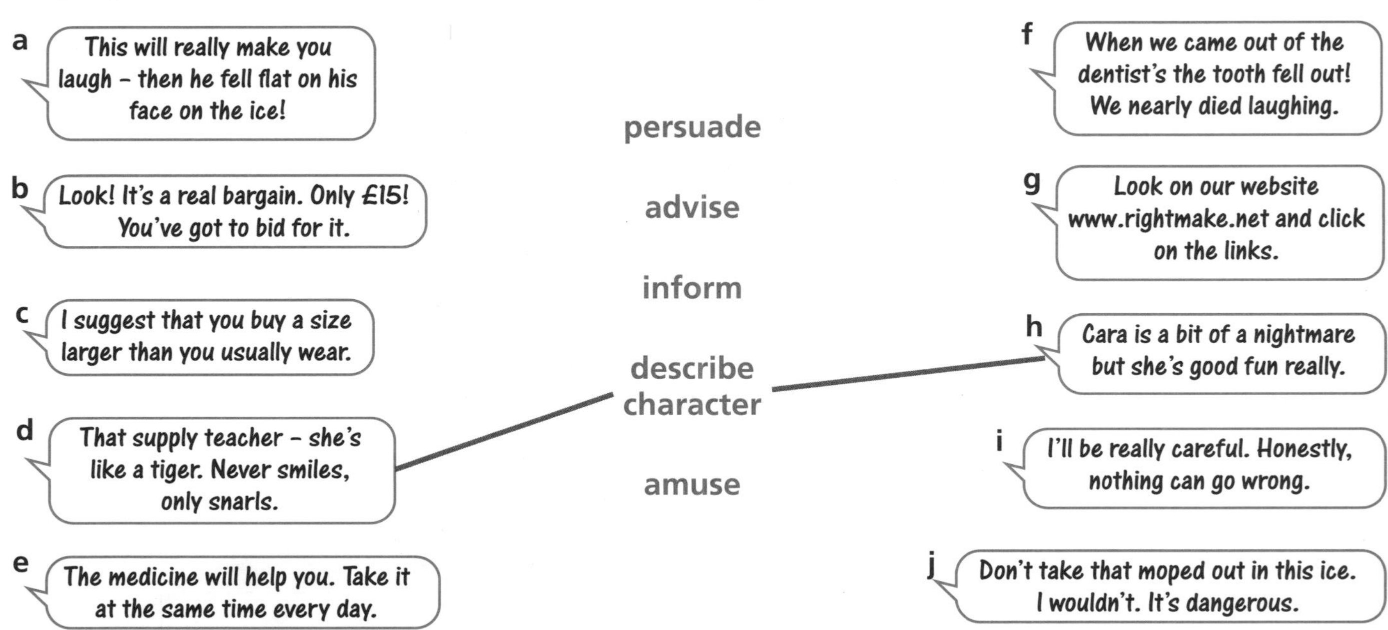

TIP ★ Read the texts aloud so you know what the writer *sounds* like.

2 Read this dialogue. Decide what the *purpose* of each speech is and fill in the number of the matching purpose given below in the box.

a) **Tania:** Jenny! Hugh's asked me to the cinema on Saturday. ☐

b) **Jenny:** Oh, go on Tania, say you'll go with him. Go on. ☐

c) **Tania:** It starts at 8.00 and finishes about half ten. He'll drive … ☐

d) **Jenny:** He's cool, Tania. Good-looking. ☐ Got spikey dark hair and is tall and thin. ☐

e) **Tania:** Well, I might … but there again I might not. We'll have to see … ☐

f) **Jenny:** Look Tania, if I were you I'd go with him. That's what I'd do. You'll not get a better offer … ☐

1 giving an opinion	**4** creating suspense	**7** giving information
2 giving advice	**5** describing a character	
3 setting the scene	**6** persuading	

TIP ★ A writer may tell you only the good or only the bad about something. The writer is in control of what information you are given.

3 Read this text, which is from Roald Dahl's autobiography *Boy*. He writes about his first experience of living away from home at St Peter's boarding school. Then use the words and phrases from the box below to fill the gaps.

> I was homesick during the whole of my first term at St Peter's. Homesickness is a bit like seasickness. You don't know how awful it is till you get it, and when you do, it hits you right in the top of the stomach and you want to die.
>
> The only comfort is that both homesickness and seasickness are instantly curable. The first goes away the moment you walk out of the school grounds and the second is forgotten as soon as the ship enters port.

a) In the first paragraph, Roald Dahl wants the reader to ______________________.

b) He uses ______________________ and ______________________ to describe what homesickness is like.

c) In the second paragraph, the writer wants to ______________________.

d) In both paragraphs, Roald Dahl wants to ______________________ the reader.

entertain	exaggeration	comparison
show that things get better	understand how awful he felt	

TIP ★ Reading in the voice of the narrator or character will help you to recognise the viewpoint.

4 Read this extract from a letter and do the exercises that follow.

> Dear Mum
>
> I wonder what you're having for tea tonight. Is it the usual Monday tea? My favourite? Shepherds Pie? I had a weird Spanish fishy thing. Pie Ella or something ... Oh Mum, I sobbed myself to sleep last night. I feel awful, I hate it here. Can't I come home? I know you think I should try for longer but I am so miserable. Please let me come home. I don't think I can stand another two weeks here. I could paint the garden fence? Or get a job.

a) Circle three things the writer is trying to do.

inform **amuse** **persuade** **create suspense**

b) Highlight three phrases in the text and label them with your answers from a.

Test yourself: practice reading tests

Reading test 1: Love Affairs

Text A

This football article is written by a sports writer for a daily newspaper.

Probably the only man I will openly say that I love ...

I am passionate about Manchester United – the team and every single one of the players. Yes, every single one of them. But THIS man I love. No, it's not Beckham. Not Ronaldo. Not Giggs … It's that super substitute*, that Norwegian 'Baby-Faced Assassin', that Ole Gunnar Solskjaer.

But now my love affair must come to an end as he retires from the game. So I find myself writing this. No more for me the agony of waiting to see the cameras turn to show him warming up on the side line and then … yes! My heart leaps. He's coming on!

Solskjaer must be the substitute who has scored more goals than any other in premiership history? Yes, he must be. He's scored 29 goals after coming on from the substitutes' bench, often with only 20 minutes of the game left. And remember the nailbiting we did in the 1999 European Cup Final? Then that heart-stopping moment at the end of the game when Sheringham headed the ball and Solskjaer flicked it into the net … GOAL!! … and we all went crazy. Unbelievably amazing! My special man had scored the winner – I basked in his glory.

A football supporter knows there are highs and there are lows. Ole brought me so high that day in May 1999, so high I'll never, ever forget it or him. He's probably the only man I will openly say that I love.

** substitute – a player who takes the place of another player during a match*

1 Solskjaer plays for a) ______________________. In 1999, he played in the final of the b) ______________________.

AF2 | 1 | 2 marks

2 *My love affair....*
Explain what the writer means by his **love affair** with Solskjaer.

____

The writer uses 'love affair' to show that he ______________________.

AF5 | 2 | 3 marks

2 In the third paragraph, the writer chooses words to show how tense and exciting the game was. Draw a line from the words to the effect of tension or excitement.

AF5 | 3 | 2 marks

shows tension

shows excitement

a heart-stopping moment

e GOAL!

b and we all went crazy

c nailbiting

d unbelievably amazing

4 Identify the writer's puposes. Tick True or False.

The writer wants to:

a) support his favourite team.	True ☐	False ☐
b) make us feel sorry for his favourite player.	True ☐	False ☐
c) say goodbye to his favourite player.	True ☐	False ☐
d) tell us about his feelings for his favourite player.	True ☐	False ☐
e) amuse us with his writing.	True ☐	False ☐

AF6 | 4 | 3 marks

5 What does each paragraph in the text do? Write the correct paragraph number in each box.

a) Gives facts and information. ☐

b) Explains why he is writing the text now. ☐

c) Explains his feelings. ☐

d) Tells us who or what the text is about. ☐

AF4 | 5 | 2 marks

Text B

This text is from a story called *Love Letters* by Kate Walker. Nick and his girlfriend, Fleur, are talking about love.

'You're so unromantic, Nick.'

'Of course I'm not unromantic!' I said, and I offered her a lick of my ice cream to prove it. She groaned and pulled her PE bag over her head. She didn't want to talk to me anymore.

When girls go quiet, that's a bad sign!

'What's *wrong*?' I asked her.

'You don't love me,' she said.

'Of course I love you,' I told her. I offered her my whole ice cream. She wouldn't take it.

'You don't love me *enough*,' she said.

How much is *enough*?

How much ice cream did it take?

'You don't write *me* letters like Clive does to Helen,' she said.

'I don't need to, I see you every day in Computers,' I said. '*And* Chemistry.'

'Clive sees Helen every day in Biology, and Textiles, and Home Science, and Assembly, and roll call,' she said, 'and he writes letters to her!'

I knew what was happening here: my girlfriend was cooling on me.

'OK,' I said, 'I'll write you a letter.'

'Aw, Nick!' She whipped her PE bag off her head.

6 Find one word in the first five lines that tells you Fleur is not happy with Nick.

____

AF5 | 6 | 1 mark

7 Fill in these gaps.

a) Nick thinks it is romantic to ______________________________.

b) Fleur thinks it is romantic to ______________________________.

AF3 | 7 | 2 marks

8 At school, when does each couple meet? Draw lines to match them up.

AF2 | 8 | 1 mark

Helen and Clive

Nick and Fleur

Computers | Biology | Textiles | Chemistry | Assembly | Home Science

9 Why are some words in the text, such as *wrong*, *enough* and *And* written in italics?

____

AF4 | 9 | 1 mark

10 Give three things you learn about Nick from this conversation and quote a short phrase as evidence.

AF6 | 10 | 3 marks

What I learn about Nick's character	Evidence from the text

Reading test 2: Emergency!

Text A

In this story Ellie describes an attack on her boyfriend, Dan, by two skinheads. They are all at a party.

The attack

The heaviest of his mates lumbers over to Dan. There's a thud, a squeal and then Dan is sprawling on the floor.

'Dan!'

'Shut up or you'll get it too,' says the skin. 'Did you pop him one, Sandy?'

'Help!' Dan screams, staggering up. His white T-shirt is stained dark red. 'He's stabbed me! I'm bleeding, look!'

Screams echo right around the room as Dan lurches forwards and then sinks to his knees.

'What have you done now, Sandy? Quick! Run for it!' the skinhead yells, shoving me aside and taking to his heels. The others follow him. No one dares stop them.

....

'Dan!' I say, bending down, clutching him, trying to prop his head on my knees. 'Someone dial 999, and get an ambulance!'

'It's OK,' says Dan, trying to sit up. 'I don't need an ambulance!'

'Are you crazy? You've been stabbed!'

'No, I haven't,' says Dan, grinning. 'Those thugs have gone, haven't they?' I thought they might run for it if they thought I was bleeding to death. I don't think that guy even had a knife. He just punched me in the stomach and I fell over.'

'But the blood!'

'Smell it,' says Dan, holding out his sopping T-shirt.

'Yuck!'

'It's the punch. I spilled it all over me.'

Girls in Love by Jacqueline Wilson

1 What does the word 'lumbers' tell you about the way the skinhead's mate moves?

'Lumbers' suggests that he moves ______________________ and

______________________ .

AF5 | 1 | 2 marks

2 In the first section, the skinhead says, 'What have you done now, Sandy?' He says this because:

★ he realises they could be in a lot of trouble. ☐

★ he wants to cause more trouble. ☐

★ he sees the blood and is upset. ☐

★ he thinks Dan has just been punched. ☐

AF3 | 2 | 1 mark

3 Find and copy a phrase in the first section that tells you the skinheads run off quickly.

____

____

AF5 | 3 | 1 mark

4 'Are you *crazy*?'
What is the effect of putting this word in italics?

____

____

AF5 | 4 | 1 mark

5 Explain how Dan has managed to trick the skinheads.

____

____

AF3 | 5 | 2 marks

6 Who makes which sound? Look at the different sounds in the passage and draw lines to match them up.

	Sound	Made by
a)	thud	skinhead
b)	squeal	people in room
c)	scream	Dan
d)	yell	Dan

AF2 | 6 | 2 marks

Text B

This text is from a first aid book.

FIRST AID: Bleeding

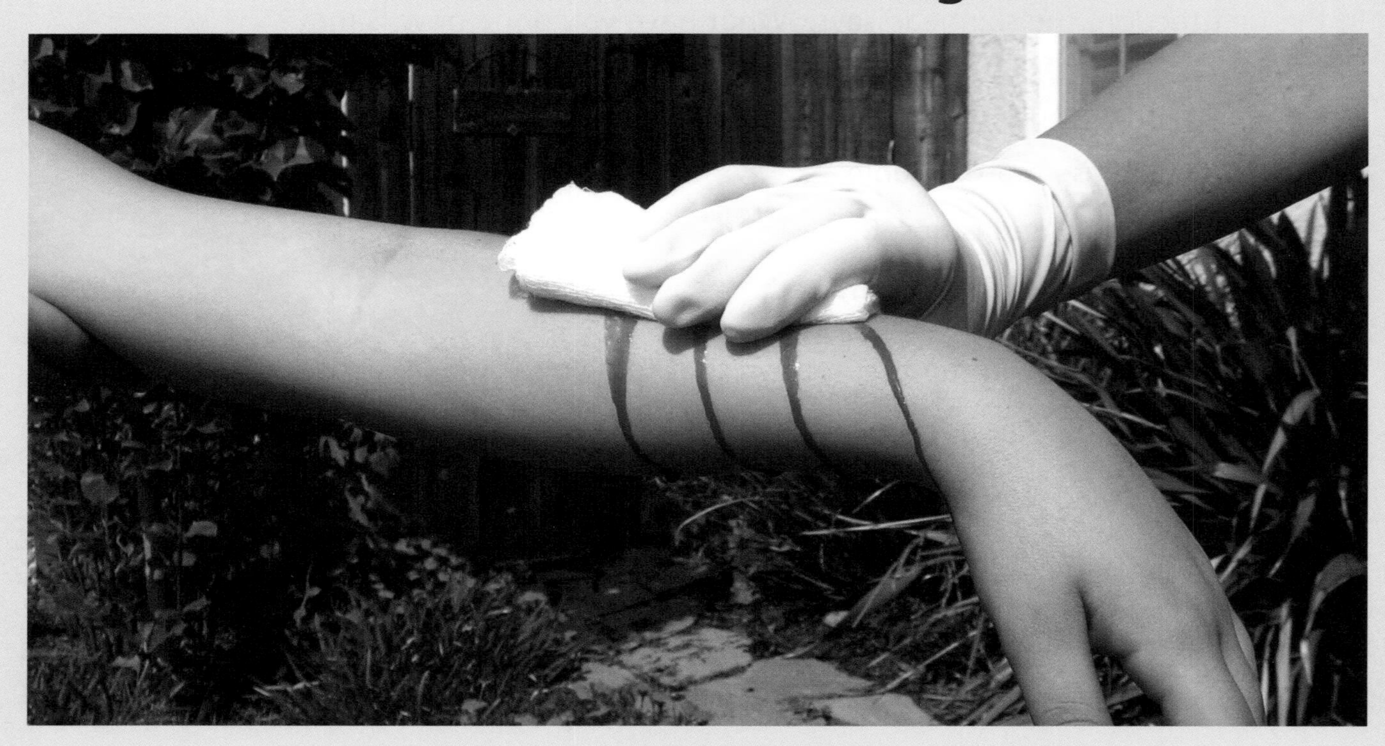

If someone is bleeding, your main priority is to stop the bleeding as quickly as possible. Pressing down on the wound and lifting the affected part of the body are what's needed. Sit the patient down. If it's an arm or a leg that's bleeding, you should use something to cover the wound, put your hand over it, squeeze it tight and raise the limb.

People may well feel shocked if the cut is bad, so they might feel dizzy. If this happens, lay them down, with their legs lifted. The last thing you want is for them to fall over while you're trying to treat the bleeding. You should call an ambulance if someone is so dizzy they can't stand up.

Dial 999 and ask for an ambulance. The ambulance control room will ask you for information so they can help you quickly. They will:

1. check the telephone number you are calling from in case you get cut off;
2. ask the exact place you are calling from to be sure of finding you;
3. ask you what the problem is;
4. ask if the patient is breathing;
5. advise you how to help the patient until the ambulance arrives;
6. tell you to lock pets (especially dogs) away before the crew gets there so they can get to the patient as quickly as possible.

7 Put these instructions in the correct order by numbering them. The first has been done for you.

AF2 — 7 — 2 marks

a) Raise the arm or leg. ☐

b) Squeeze tight. ☐

c) Cover the wound. ☐

d) Put your hand over it. ☐

e) Sit the patient down. 1

8 Look at the numbered list in the text. Give two problems that might slow down the ambulance crew's arrival.

AF3 — 8 — 2 marks

a) ______________________________

b) ______________________________

9 Why does the writer use numbered points in one section of the text?

AF4 — 9 — 2 marks

____

____

____

10 Who is this text written for? Circle one answer and then explain why you think this.

AF6 — 10 — 3 marks

a doctor   ordinary people

____

____

____

____

____

____

Introduction to writing skills

The following section in this book (pages 40–57) will help you to revise and practise one writing skill at a time so that you can achieve a Level 4 standard of writing. These skills will help you add **interest** and **accuracy** to your written communication and achieve Level 4.

Sentence structure and punctuation

Think about *building* a text as building a wall. It needs planning and all the right materials.

The features of sentence construction (pages 40–47) include the following.

- **Connectives:** Level 4 writers use a variety of connectives, including 'because', 'when', 'if' as well as 'and' and 'but'.
- **Adjectives and adverbs:** Level 4 writers use a variety of adjectives and adverbs to add detail to their writing.
- **Punctuation:** Level 4 writers use full stops and capital letters accurately.

Text structure and organisation

In this section of the book (starting on page 48), you will revise and practise skills that will help you to achieve Level 4 organisation and development of the whole text. This section shows you how to communicate in a **clear** and **interesting** way with the reader.

- **Improving the organisation of ideas** will help you to organise paragraphs by using topic sentences.
- **Developing an idea** will help you to build up paragraphs with relevant and interesting ideas.

Reader and purpose

In this section of the book (page 52–57), you will revise and practise skills to help you address the needs of readers of your writing.

For example, you should write differently to your best friend from writing to your local MP! A letter has different conventions to a story.

★ **Writing for a reader** will help you to focus on the needs of a reader.

★ **Using interesting words for effect** will help you to practise using a wider vocabulary.

★ **Choosing an appropriate form and style** will help you to choose whether an informal or formal style should be used for your writing.

All of the skills you revise and practise here are assessed and marked by examiners in the National Tests. Practising these skills will help you to improve the quality of all your writing, including writing for the National Tests.

★ Finally, a longer writing task and a shorter writing task, similar to those in the National Tests, give you the chance to practise the format of the Key Stage 3 tests. You can mark them yourself using the self-assessment sheet (see page 61).

Using a wider variety of connectives

Level 3 writers generally use *and*, *but* and *because* to link ideas in sentences.
Level 4 writers use a limited range of connectives including *when* and *if*.

1 Practise using **and but because** to make a link between the parts of these sentences. It's not as easy as you think!

Turn up the heating …	**and** let's stay indoors. a) ________ it's snowing outside. b) ________ not for too long.
This is a difficult time for Ronesco the footballer …	c) ________ it shows. d) ________ he's not scoring any goals. e) ________ he's still scoring goals.
The T-shirt is worn out …	f) ________ I still like it. g) ________ I've had it so long. h) ________ I now wish I'd bought two of them.

2 Now join the beginnings to the end using **and but because**.

My car is not going very fast *because* a) The engine sounds all right ________ b) This car has a flat battery ________	it needs repairing.
c) Simon has bought a new game ________ d) John saw the new game ________ e) Carl didn't ask for the new game ________	he wanted one.
f) The letters didn't arrive yesterday ________ g) Granny and Grandad won't visit us next week ________ h) The builders came to repair the wall yesterday ________	they came today.

TIP ★ The connective **and** is often used far too much in Level 3 writing KS3. Try to use other connectives.

TIP ★ Use connectives **when, if** and **so**. They are easy to use and help to make your writing more interesting.

3 This is a review about a computer game. It is well-written apart from using **and** far too much. Replace the use of **and** with the connectives given in the boxes that follow.

New Game for Skate Fans

Grind is a computer game about skateboarding and it is the best game I have played on the computer. I enjoyed Grind very much, ~~and~~ a) ________ I thought I should pass on my comments. First you click on start ~~and~~ b) ________ you choose who is going to take part in the competition. You can choose famous skateboarders ~~and~~ c) ________ you can make up your own names if you want. It's up to you. The computer sets up a course for you ~~and~~ d) ________ you can create your own course. I think it is better to do it yourself ~~and~~ e) ________ that might be because I have played it a lot. I try to put in lots of difficult jumps ~~and~~ f) ________ it's more exciting.

or	but	because	then	so

The game can seem easy ~~and~~ g) ________ be careful because you lose points for every mistake. You lose points if you lose the board ~~and~~ h) ________ go round the course the wrong way. The lowest number of penalty points wins and my best score is 23. I am into skateboarding ~~and~~ i) ________ that could be why I liked Grind. I would definitely recommend it to people ~~and~~ j) ________ only if they like skateboarding. If you do, then it's a great game!

so	or	but	but

TIP ★ Don't use the same connective in two sentences next to each other.

4 Write about your favourite way to spend a day using as many different connectives as you can.

Adding detail by using adjectives

Level 3 writers add detail by using some simple adjectives.
Level 4 writers add detail by using some interesting adjectives.

When you are describing things, you need adjectives to make them clearer and tell the reader more about them.

1 Write down as many words as you can to describe the things in the picture, e.g. colourful clothes.

2 Adverts use lots of **positive adjectives**. If you are selling something, you need to say how **good** your item is so that people will bid for it.

Choose an adjective from this box below to improve these descriptions.

real	dark	brand-new	clever	useful	coloured	top-quality	cold

trainers	a) ____________ skateboard trainers. Light b) ____________ suede. Size 8.
travel guide	c) ____________ guide to Egypt.
watch	One d) ____________ watch. Rolex-style with e) ____________ diamonds.

TIP ★ Avoid using **good**, **bad** or **nice**. Take time to think of a word to **help the reader imagine** what you are describing.

3 Write adverts for three things that you might want to sell.

TIP ★ Imagine the situation in your head. Think about how things look.

4 This is a letter of complaint about a holiday that went badly wrong. Fill in the gaps in the first paragraph with negative adjectives from the box. Then choose your own for C–F.

Dear Sirs,

I am writing to complain about my trip with you to Portugal. Firstly, we were picked up at the airport on a a) ______ coach driven by a b) ______ driver.

teenage	sensible	modern	battered

When we set eyes on the c) ______ hotel our hearts sank. The d) ______ girl on the reception desk was as good as useless. It took us hours to be given our room keys. The e) ______ rooms were a disgrace and the f) ______ balcony was a danger to the public.

I hope that you will be able to understand how all these problems spoiled our holiday and that you will refund some of our money.

Yours faithfully

D.Thompson

D. Thompson

5 Look at this detective story. Choose your own adjective for each gap.

Bill Beat opened the a) ______ office door. He'd been in the police force a long time and was a b) ______ detective. With a keen eye he looked around the c) ______ room. There was a table, a d) ______ stool, and a e) ______ mirror hanging on the wall. Not many places to hide a bag of diamonds! He knew they had to be in there, but where? He whistled thoughtfully. Then it dawned on him! Under the certificate! He lifted it quickly from its f) ______ nail. He was right. There was a hole with g) ______ newspaper pushed firmly into it. He eased the paper out and saw a h) ______ bag. He weighed the bag in his policeman's hand and whistled again. Then he tipped out the ten sparkling diamonds and whistled for the third time.

Using adverbs to help a reader

Level 3 writers sometimes use simple adverbs.
Level 4 writers use simple adverbs to add detail and organise.

A sailor needs help to find the way across the sea.

A reader needs help to find a way through a piece of writing.

TIP
★ Using adverbs will give order and extra detail to your writing.

1 Use the adverbs in the boxes below to organise and add extra detail to this piece about a science experiment. Some can be used more than once.

a) ______ I collected all the equipment I needed for the experiment. Then I measured b) ______ 20 ml of water into the flask. I wore gloves and used tongs to c) ______ hold the flask over the heat. The water d) ______ began to get hot. As soon as the water began to boil, I started the timer. I let the water boil for e) ______ four minutes. f) ______ I remembered that I must not put a hot flask on the bench. So I carried it g) ______ to a mat to go cold. h) ______ I looked at the amount of water that was left in the flask and wrote down the result.

Adverbs to give extra detail

safely tightly luckily approximately exactly

Adverbs to organise ideas

firstly finally soon

2 Adverbs tell us when, where or how something is done.

> Tim finished his work **last night**. (when)
>
> Samantha rode the pony **wildly**. (how)

Highlight the adverbs in each sentence and tick the correct box to show whether they are **when** or **how** adverbs (or both).

	Highlight the adverbs	**when**	**how**
a)	The soldiers were waiting patiently in the trenches.		
b)	Major Holme suddenly ordered the attack.		
c)	The cup smashed noisily onto the floor.		
d)	Nina muttered angrily to herself.		
e)	First, Laura carefully cut off her sister's ponytail while she lay sleeping.		
f)	Next, she gently drew a moustache in pen on her face.		
g)	Mrs Derek marched furiously up to the headmaster.		
h)	'My John will soon be leaving here,' she loudly announced.		

TIP ★ Adverbs are not difficult to use. The trick is to *remember* to use them!

3 Write out the alphabet. Think of an adverb for each letter.

A awfully

B bravely

C ______________

4 Now continue this short story using as many adverbs as you can. Tick them off on your alphabet list.

The Rescue

Carlo lay down wearily on his prison bed. Hopefully, today would mean a rescue …

Using full stops and capital letters to mark sentences

Level 3 writers often use full stops and capital letters accurately.
Level 4 writers use full stops and capital letters accurately.

Do you put the lid back on the toothpaste? Millions of people drive others mad by *not* doing this. Why?

Because they are forgetful, they don't care or are just too lazy.

Same with **full stops**. You probably know how to use them, but if you don't use them accurately, your punctuation will not progress to Level 4.

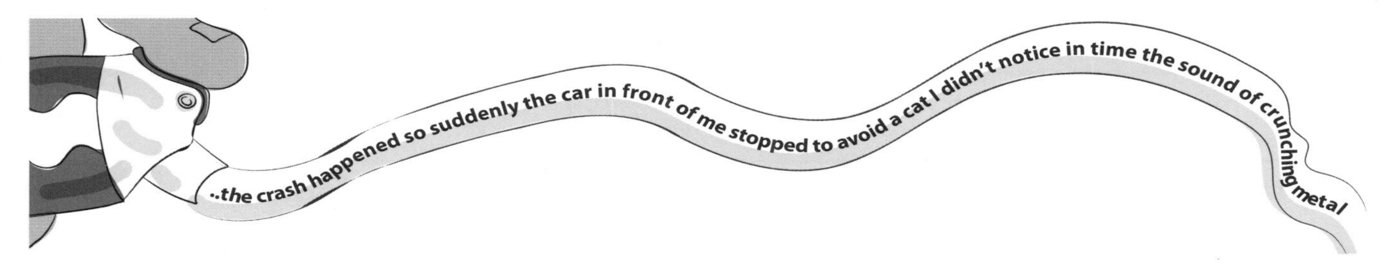

1 Look at these messages. Can you make sense of them?
Copy them out correctly with full stops, question marks and capital letters.

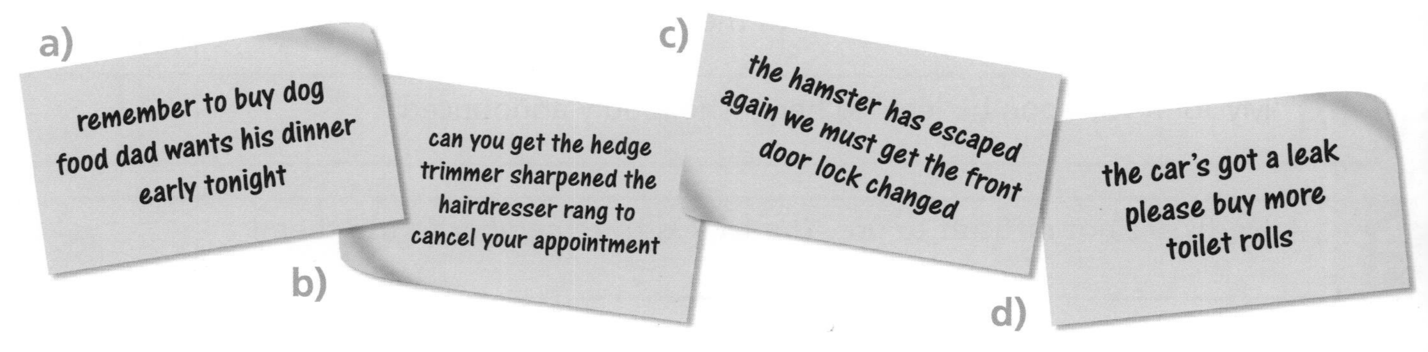

2 The story below is well-written apart from the punctuation. Mark the sentences with capital letters and full stops or question marks. The number of sentences needed is given below it.

a) Amina decided to go exploring she made her way past the dustbins and up the narrow alleyway to the Brighton Road.
[2]

b) It was a warm day and she felt very lazy she sat on the seat at the roadside a couple of cats were sunning themselves on a wall.
[3]

c) She heard a clatter and a bang behind her it sounded like someone had dropped a dustbin lid she turned to see a group of girls watching her they did not look altogether friendly.
[4]

d) Amina felt uncomfortable what were the girls up to she decided to stand up and make her way home the group gathered to watch her Amina didn't look back but walked into a shop she did not fancy being alone on the street.
[6]

TIP
★ Read the sentences to yourself. This will help you to find the breaks.

3 In this part of the same story the writer has gone mad with full stops! Tick the correct full stops and cross out the incorrect ones. Add capital letters where needed.

a) The leader of the gang seemed to be the small girl. in the black T-shirt. she was chewing gum. and carrying a large shiny red handbag.

b) The other small one was obviously her sister. because their faces were so alike. both had dark brown eyes and. dead straight hair.

c) Would they give her any trouble? Amina smiled nervously and moved past. them back towards the alleyway. and home. she hoped they wouldn't follow her.

d) Her heart pounded. she decided to do nothing but she would ask her cousin about them. later on. she had been silly to go out alone. on her first day. she realised this now.

4 Capital letters are also needed for names – countries, people, brand names, etc.

a) Go through this newspaper article and highlight all the *names* that should have capital letters. Can you find eight different names?

Spider girls trapped

1 Police have arrested two members of one of chile's most notorious gangs they are called the 'spider girls'.

2 The all-girl gang of teenagers is famous for climbing up buildings in santiago their aim is to rob luxury apartments while the owners are out of the city.

3 They lurk in gardens spotting open windows and waiting for their chance they throw ropes up to the balcony railings and climb up the next bit is easy they just walk through the open windows.

4 Between january and august 2005, they made off with thousands of pounds worth of jewellery and clothes by dior, chanel and armani why did they do it because they wanted money for new clothes.

b) Using a different colour highlighter, mark the sentence breaks with a stroke (/).

If you need some help, this table tells you how many sentences there are in each paragraph. But don't look unless you have to.

paragraph	1	2	3	4
sentences	2	2	4	3

TIP ★ Make full stops your main focus for one whole week. You will be surprised at the praise you will get!

Improving the organisation of ideas

Level 3 writers sometimes use paragraphs, but they need more organisation.
Level 4 writers organise ideas around a main, or topic, sentence in a paragraph.

TIP
★ The first sentence of the paragraph shows the reader what the rest of the paragraph will be about.

1 Draw lines to link the opening sentences to the rest of the paragraph. One has been done as an example.

Opening sentence containing the topic	Ideas which develop the topic
There's too much football on TV.	**i)** I knew he was ill because he wasn't eating his food. I thought I had better find out what the problem was.
a) I had to take my dog to the vets last week.	**ii)** The exams have finished and we go on lots of different trips. It's great because we know the summer holidays are about to start.
b) My summer holiday was terrible.	**iii)** It gets boring after a while. I think different sports should be on. More tennis would be a good idea because lots of people like it.
c) The last week of the summer term is the best.	**iv)** It rained all week and was really cold. One day our tent was blown down because it was so windy.

2 Write topic sentences for these paragraphs.

a) Mobile phones ____.

Lots of people say that teenagers spend too much time texting their friends, but that's how we communicate these days. Years ago people wrote letters and no one criticised them. We just use mobile phones instead. It shouldn't be a problem.

b) Riding a bike ____.

It gets you from one place to another without harming the environment. It keeps you fit and helps you get to know your home area.

3 Write a short paragraph (about three more sentences) to build up each of these topic sentences.

a) Some people say that your years in school are the best of your life.

b) The issue of testing medicines on animals always gets people arguing.

c) Sport is not for everyone.

4 Read this review. Then highlight the topic sentences and mark paragraph breaks with two strokes (//). There should be four topic sentences and four paragraphs. One of each has been done for you.

STAR SEARCH

***Star Search* is a new TV programme. It is a talent-spotting show. After the first programme, viewers were invited to visit the show's website and say what they thought about the show. Read this message from the site.**

Review

Firstly, there's nothing new in your Star Search programme. There are already loads of shows like that. Three celebrities or stars sit there and vote on who is the best new act. // There is one way it could improve and that is by getting some new stars to be the judges. You need younger and more famous stars to get people to watch it. It needs to be on at a different time. It starts when people are still busy. A lot of people are trying to get home from work or school then. Starting two hours later would be better. I hope you make those changes. If you don't, I think the programme will fail.

Developing an idea

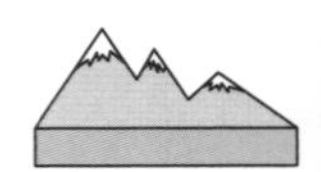

Level 3 writers use simple ideas.
Level 4 writers use relevant ideas and develop some of these ideas.

Planning

A good plan helps you to develop ideas before you start.

★ Thinking time before you start writing is very important.

1 Look at this writing task. Then complete the planning exercises to develop some ideas.

Your class is preparing a brief information leaflet for new pupils at your school. Your job is to write about school times, food, and what to do if you get lost.

a) Add the ideas given in the box below to develop the main points in this mind map. An example has been given.

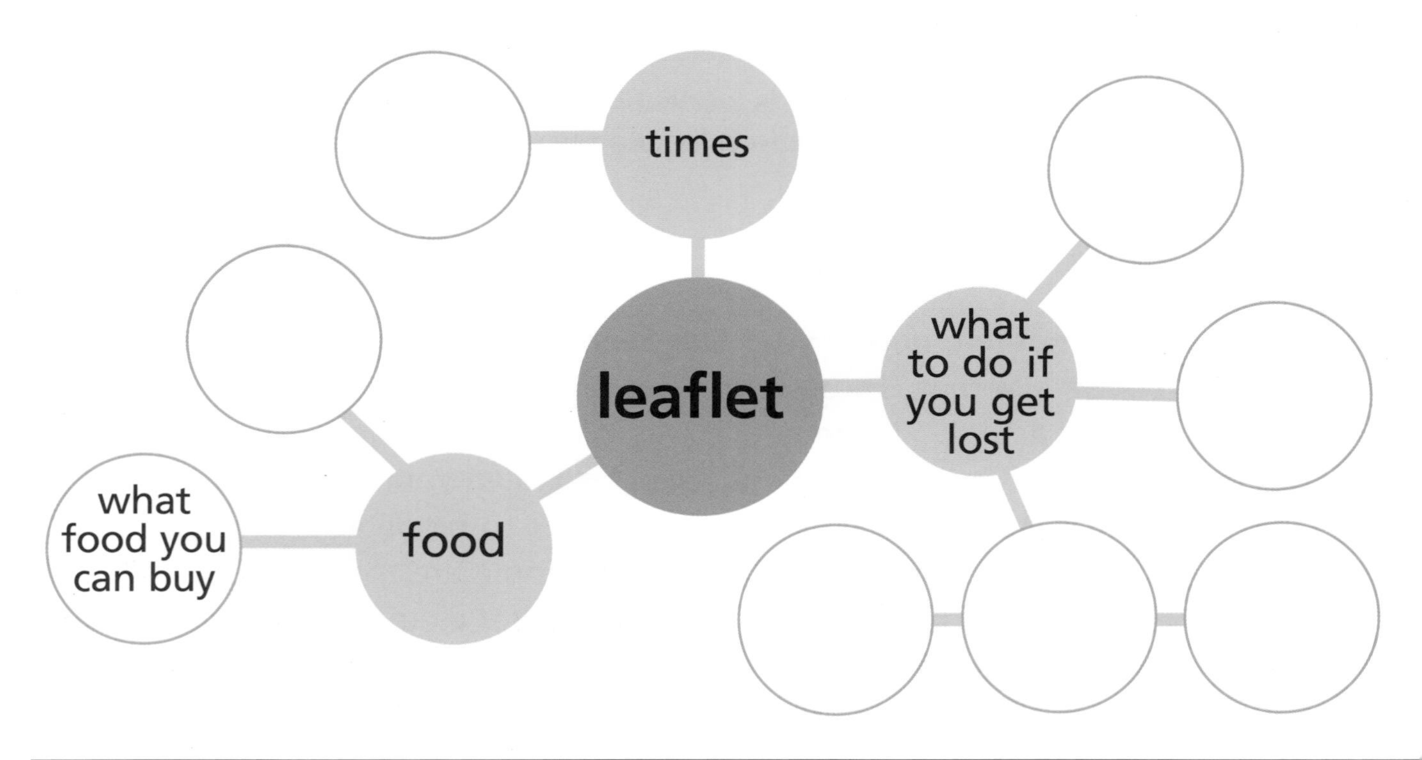

people you can ask for help	what the staff are like	where canteen is
times of the day	information on noticeboards	where the office is
what the food is like		

b) Which section could not be developed?

2 Read this pupil information leaflet to see how ideas are developed into sections.

Welcome to Highlea School	Eating	Lost?
We are a big but very friendly school. You may be a little nervous at first but this information will help you to find your way around. **Times** School starts at 8.45 a.m. Break is at 11.10 a.m. Lunch is at 12.45 p.m. School finishes at 3.45 p.m.	At break or lunch you can go to the canteen in the school hall. This is through the door to the left of the main entrance. The canteen serves lots of different foods including hot and cold meals. The snacks at breaktime are pretty good and follow the school's healthy eating policy. There are things like baked potatoes, bacon rolls and juices. At lunchtime, they sell a full range of typical school meals. Try the pasta – it's great!	If you get lost, don't panic. Most people will help you out and some will even show you where to go if they want to miss a bit of their own lesson! Or, you could go to the school office and they will help. Or, look in your school diary at the map at the back. Nearly everybody gets lost once or twice in the first week, so don't worry. Ask!

How many sentences are used to develop:

a) where the canteen is?

b) what kind of food is sold?

c) what to do if you get lost?

TIP

★ Mind maps will help you to see which ideas can be developed.

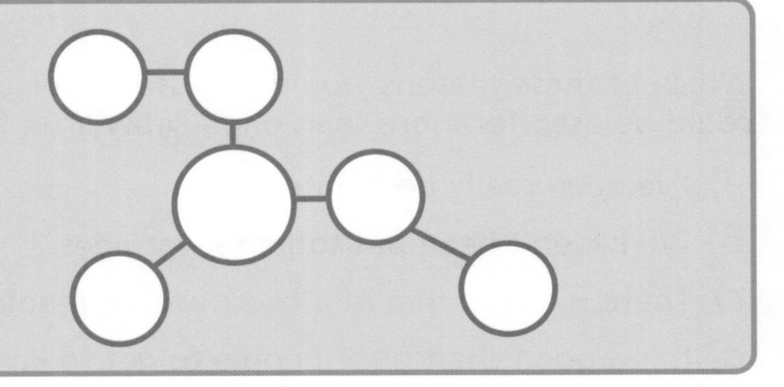

3 Plan your answers for these writing tasks. Try to develop at least two ideas for each task.

a) On a separate piece of paper, write a description of a place that makes you nervous. Describe:

★ where it is;

★ what it's like;

★ how it makes you feel.

b) On a separate piece of paper, write a letter of complaint to a restaurant. Mention:

★ when you visited;

★ what the food was like;

★ what you want them to do about it.

Writing for a reader

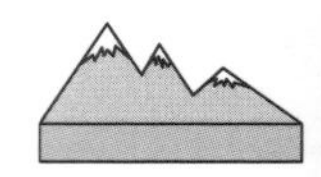

Level 3 writers write about the subject but do not show that they can think about the reader.

Level 4 writers are aware of the needs of the reader.

TIP
Writing for a reader means thinking about:
- ★ who the reader is.
- ★ what the reader needs to know.
- ★ how to help the reader understand ideas in the writing.

1 When writing the following three emails, how would you treat the different readers?

An email to persuade:
- ★ your parents to take you to the cinema;
- ★ your best friends to go to the cinema with you;
- ★ your teacher to take your class on a trip to the cinema.

Which of these reasons would you use to persuade the different readers? (Some of the reasons could be used for more than one.) Draw lines from the reasons to the readers.

a) I've been really good lately.
b) We haven't been out together for ages.
c) There is a new film of a book we are reading in English.
d) It is a good chance for people to get to know each other.
e) It is quite a cheap evening out.
f) You will love this film.
g) I'll treat you to a night out.
h) It's a film for all ages.
i) We used to love cinema visits when I was little.

TIP
- ★ Writers choose different reasons and different language, because they know the best way to write for different readers.

2 This task is about changes to the school canteen.

The new cook wants to have healthy food in the school canteen. Her idea is to stop selling burgers and start selling tuna sandwiches. But first she wants to know what pupils think, so she has put a box for their comments on the canteen counter.

This is Dave's response for the comments box.

No one will use the canteen any more, I like my burgers. This idea is stupid. You're trying to force us to eat food we don't like. You can't tell us what to eat. My dad agrees with me and he says you're bossy. Next week I'm going down the road to the burger bar. I hate tuna but I like burger and chips.

a) Highlight sentences about **Dave** in one colour.

b) Highlight sentences about **the food** in another colour.

Dave's comments do not consider the needs of the reader – the school cook! He does not make any positive suggestions; he only writes about himself.

3 Read Adam's response. It is more polite, and also provides the school cook with reasons and ideas that will help her to decide what to do. It considers her needs as a reader.

Label each paragraph with how it helps the reader to understand Adam's opinions.
The first one has been done for you.

- **A** Considers the opposite point of view.
- **B** States his own point of view.
- **C** Explains how burgers could be good.
- **D** Brings ideas to a clear end.
- **E** Adds a new idea to his comment about burgers.

I don't agree with your plan to stop selling burgers. I think there are lots of reasons for keeping them on the menu. (B)

1 Firstly, good burgers are not really unhealthy food. It just depends on the meat. If it is low fat meat, it will help us stay healthy. ( )

2 Salad is also healthy and burgers are a good way of getting teenagers to eat salad. The old cook never used to put any salad in the burgers. If you mix the salad with a tasty sauce, we'll be happy to eat lettuce. ( )

3 Your idea for tuna sandwiches might work. Make them taste good and people will choose them. A few people do like fish but most of us want a choice for our dinner. ( )

4 Finally, I hope you will put burgers and tuna on the menu next week. If you do, you will have lots of happy customers! ( )

4 Write two letters – one to your headteacher and one to your friend – to persuade them to donate money to your favourite charity.

Using interesting words for effect

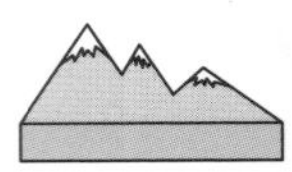

Level 3 writers use simple words.

Level 4 writers use a wider range of words and try to use some for effect on the reader.

TIP ★ Do not simply use the first word that comes into your head. Check that it is interesting and adds detail to your writing.

1 Use your *imagination* to think of words for the pictures to tell a reader what the *characters* are like. Give at least four ideas for each character.

TIP ★ In a story, the characters belong to you. Give your reader enough information to understand them.

2 Use your *imagination* to add words to describe the *actions* in this picture. An example has been done for you.

glancing back

TIP ★ Using interesting words helps your reader – and gets you good marks!

3 Practise using your vocabulary to add detail to this detective story opening and answer the question below.

choose your character

Inspector Foreman

Jane Pepper-Davis

Dan Jackson

develop some ideas

elderly, always cleaning his glasses

rich, attractive, used to getting her own way

young detective, brainy, a bit arrogant

Which words do you think best describe these characters? Choose some of the words here to help your reader picture the characters:

old, shuffled, pretty, crafty, glamorous, cross, wealthy, raced, cunning, unhappy, impatient, arrogant, rich, hurried, bossy, walked slowly, elderly, annoyed, in a hurry, miserable

TIP ★ One word is not always 'better' than another. The most important thing is to choose the best word for the situation.

Choosing an appropriate form and style

Level 3 writers write as they would speak to someone.
Level 4 writers can change their style depending on the task, e.g. letter, story, newspaper report.

One main choice of style is between formal and informal writing.

★ Informal – similar to how you speak but not quite the same. You have to give more detail to make up for not being able to use tone of voice or gestures when writing.

★ Formal – think 'posh' or using words as a TV newsreader would!

1 The following exercises are about formal and informal phrases.

a) Spot the difference between these formal and informal phrases used in letters. Mark the phrases with F (Formal) or I (Informal).

Thank you for your letter about ... F

Thanks for your letter. I

i) I'll finish now as I'm running out of space. ☐
ii) If you have any further questions, please contact me again. ☐
iii) I look forward to hearing from you. ☐
iv) I'm writing to ask you a favour. ☐
v) Write again soon! ☐
vi) It was lovely to hear from you. ☐
vii) It was great to get your letter. ☐
viii) Thank you so much for writing. ☐
ix) I wish to complain about ... ☐
x) I am writing with reference to your letter ... ☐

b) Are these 'rules' for formal writing true (T) or false (F)?

i) Do not use abbreviations, e.g. I'm, He's. ☐
ii) Use common words, e.g. want, ask. ☐
iii) Use short, simple sentences. ☐

c) Write out a list of the correct 'rules'.

2 Change these informal sentences into more formal language, using the words in the box to help you. An example has been given.

I've seen a **great** film. **You'll love it.**

I have seen an **excellent** film. **You will be sure to love it.**

a) My dad thinks computer games are rubbish.

b) I'll see you next week.

c) If you want, you can come round tomorrow.

would like to	father	waste of time	will	look forward to	visit	wish	are welcome to

TIP ★ Most examination writing styles expect you to use a more formal style as it lets you show off your writing skills.

3 Complete a few further exercises on informal and formal styles.

a) Write a brief character summary of your friend using your own, informal style.

b) Now, write a report on your friend by your English teacher.

c) Highlight all the formal language you use in the report by the teacher.

TIP ★ Imagine that you are trying to impress your reader and your writing will generally sound more formal.

How to tackle the writing task

It's the start of the test: read the writing task carefully and don't panic! Before you start writing you need the answer to FOUR questions.

WHO is the WRITER? Are you writing as yourself, or as another person?
WHO is the READER? Are you writing this for anyone in particular (apart from the examiner, of course)?
WHAT FORM of writing is it? Is it a letter? A report? A story? Or something else?
WHAT is its PURPOSE? Is it to inform? To describe? To persuade? Or something else?

The answers to these four questions are always in the task: LOOK for them. Sometimes you have to work it out from clues.

These four things – WRITER, READER, FORM and PURPOSE – will have a big impact on what and how you write.

★ They will affect your ideas and the sort of detail you include.
★ They will affect the words and phrases you choose.
★ They will affect how you organise your ideas.
★ They will affect your tone (the sort of voice you use – polite, friendly, etc.).

It's just like when we talk – we change the tone, the words we use and what we say according to **who** we are, **who** we are speaking to and **why** we are talking.

Think of these writers:

A A businesswoman writes a letter to her bank to explain why she needs a loan and to persuade them to lend her some money.
B A teenage boy writes an email to his best friend to tell him what was good and bad about a rock festival he went to.
C A journalist writes a report for a newsaper about a heroic act.
D A novelist writes the opening chapter of a novel to send to a publisher.

Ask yourself the four questions: **WRITER? READER? FORM? PURPOSE?** for the four writers, **A, B, C, D**. In some cases you have to work out the answer for yourself. Fill in this table with the answers.

	Who is the writer?	Who is the reader?	What is the form?	What is the purpose?
A				
B				
C				
D				

All writers have to make their writing interesting for the reader. They all have to include details and develop their ideas. But there will be some differences.

Test yourself: practice writing tasks

Longer writing task

Work on your own.
You have 45 minutes for the longer writing task in your Key Stage 3 writing test.
Use about 10 minutes for planning. Allow five minutes for making changes at the end.

inform, explain, describe

SATURDAY SCHOOL

Dear students
I am thinking about changing the times of the school day.
I suggest that we finish at lunchtime each day. We can use Saturday mornings to make up for the extra time off in the afternoons.
What do you think? Please write to me explaining your opinions so that I can make the best decision.
Yours sincerely
Mrs T. Johnson
Headteacher

Write a letter to the headteacher explaining your opinions. Use the planning sheet on page 60 to help you organise your answer.

Shorter writing task

You have 30 minutes for the shorter writing task in your Key Stage 3 writing test.

imagine, entertain, explore

IMAGINE

Use this picture to help you imagine the **opening** of a story.

Write two to three paragraphs to describe the location and introduce the characters.

Planning sheet for longer writing task

Make notes about your ideas.

Advantages of the changes to the school day

Disadvantages of the changes

People who would be affected by the changes

Ending

Self-assessment sheet

★ Look at the descriptions in the Level 4 section of the table.

★ In your work, find examples of the descriptions in the table.

★ Highlight the description in the table, and an example in your work.

★ If you have at least ten of the Level 4 descriptions highlighted, you have achieved Level 4.

★ In a different colour, highlight what you still need to improve.

Level	Sentence structure	Punctuation	Paragraph organisation	Organisation inside paragraphs	Effect on the reader
3	I mainly use simple sentences. I mainly use *and* and *but* to connect ideas inside my sentences. I sometimes refer to the different points in time, e.g. past, present.	I use full stops and capital letters. Sometimes I use question marks and exclamation marks. I often use commas to join two sentences, when I should use full stops to separate them. I use some speech punctuation if it is needed.	I sometimes use paragraphs. My paragraphs are written as I think them. They are not in a particular order. I have tried to use an introduction and a conclusion.	The ideas in my paragraphs are not in a particular order. I sometimes use words such as *then* or *and* to add ideas. It can be difficult to see how an idea in one of my paragraphs links to the next one.	I give one idea and then move on to the next idea. I use basic words such as *think*, *chase*, *large*. In the longer writing task, I sometimes forget I am writing to the headteacher. In the shorter writing task, I sometimes forget I am writing a story for a reader.
4	I use different lengths and kinds of sentences. I use *because*, *when* and *if* to connect ideas inside my sentences. I can refer to different points in time, e.g. past, present and future without mistakes.	Most of my sentences have correct full stops or question marks. I use commas for items in a list. I sometimes use commas to separate two parts of a sentence, e.g. *If you go there, you will see …* When I use speech, my speech marks are mostly correctly placed.	I use paragraphs to group my ideas. My paragraphs are in a logical order, but I haven't made that order clear to my reader. The opening and closing of my writing is clear.	I use a main idea and then add similar ideas to it. I add new ideas to the main idea using *also* or *then*. I use words such as *Next*, *Secondly*, *Finally* to make a link with the next paragraph.	I sometimes add detail to an idea by developing it in the next sentence. I use some words which interest my reader such as *suggest*, *attractive*, *patient*. In both tasks, I remember who my audience is.

Reading skills

Pages 10–11: Finding information in a text (1)

1 breathe; smell; pick up (food); suck up water
2 AFRICAN: fan-shaped ears; ears up to 1.5 metres wide; two lips on trunk
ASIAN: one lip on trunk; triangular ears; smaller type of elephant
3 Jackal eats: fruit, grasses, dead flesh;
Fennec fox eats: lizards, insects
4 **a)** no **b)** kitchen stool **c)** a fox
d) left/went out

Pages 12–13: Finding information in a text (2)

1 **a)** university **b)** quick **c)** cheap **d)** flour **e)** salt
2 **a) i)** turkey curry **ii)** broccoli **iii)** apple
2 **b) i)** chargrilled peppers and baked onions in a tomato pasta
ii) baby new carrots with parsley
iii) banana ice cream with chocolate sauce
3 Charlie: Hot and spicy
Abdul: Cheese and tomato
Tom: Three cheese
Nick: Hot and spicy
4 **a)** under 16 **b)** fat, salt, sugar **c)** 39 million
d) junk food, 9

Pages 14–15: What does the writer mean but not tell you directly? (1)

1 **a)** sad; disappointed **b)** old; injured
c) lazy; crafty
2 **a)** angry **b)** is pleased about something
c) about to attack
3 **a)** True: luckily it wasn't
b) False: seriously no good
c) True: calls everyone 'dude'
d) True: excellent coach/My game has really improved
4 **a)** entertaining, applauding, cheering
b) the clown prince; the joker of the tennis world

Pages 16–17: What does the writer mean but not tell you directly? (2)

1 **a)** charged (up the steps)/piled out
b) beamed **c)** over at last
2 Don't rush because you have plenty of time in a day's visit.
3 teeth showing in a snarl
4 **a)** doesn't really want
b) quivering lips/shock her parents/(mother's question) was almost more than she could bear
c) used to her
d) clues that tell you they are not reacting to her with shock but very normally: as if running away were a perfectly natural thing to do; enquired Ramona's mother politely
e) almost more than Ramona could bear, quivering lips
f) heartless
5 Look for words/phrases that give you clues/evidence.

Pages 18–19: Finding patterns in a text (1)

1 **a)** title **b)** subtitle **c)** love life
d) action – what to do
2 *Show this to your teacher.*
3 title: quickly catches reader's attention; para 1: describes suffering; para 2: asks for money; para 3: offers hope; para 4: gives a promise
4 *Show your teacher.*

Pages 20–21: Finding patterns in a text (2)

1 Give your opinion.
2 **a)** First of all, he describes the movements and the fun. Then he tells you he was sick
b) First of all she describes being sick. Then she tells you about the movements and how it was fun on the rides
c) Your own answer with a reason.
3 **a)/b)** *Show these to your teacher.*
4 **a)** father **b)** mother
c) He wants to show someone else's reaction to the father/the event.
5 **a)** Mama handed him the passports and smiled. But the hand with which she was holding her handbag was squeezing it into terrible contortions.
b) It brings tension/danger to the text./Without the sentences, nothing exciting or dangerous would be shown.

Pages 22–23: Understanding why the writer chooses a word

1 desperate/worried/devastated.
Check with your teacher if you think you have found others.
2 Positive: well-dressed; smart pin-stripe suit
Negative: small, piggy eyes; frayed; stained
Neutral: button nose; still unread; anxiously
3 **a) bullying** as stronger/more deliberate than **bossy**
b) house is just a building, **home** is a good place to be/live
4 *Check with your teacher.*
5 **a)** Suggests that the cold air is more dangerous/capable of killing.
b) Suggests how sharp/cutting/painful the wind is.

Pages 24–25: Understanding why writers sometimes use very short sentences

1 **a)** But he woke Cassy. Cassy sat up slowly.
b) Cassy
2 **a)** speed up the action
b) bring the action to a close
c) emphasise a feeling
3 **a)** Bones cracked. Cars swerved.
Horns sounded. A bus glanced past.
b) i) Highlight the noise
ii) Show lots of different things happening all around them

Pages 26–27: Identifying the writer's purpose (1)

1 **a)** inform/create suspense **b)** inform
c) advise/persuade **d)** give an opinion
2 **a)** create tension **b)** words such as screeched, scrabbling; thrashing
3 **a)** entertain **b)** parking competition for blind people; the only possible way out would be through the sun roof.

Pages 28–29: Identifying the writer's purpose (2)

1 a, i: persuade b, j: advise c, g: inform
d, f: amuse
2 **a)** 3 setting the scene **b)** 6 persuading
c) 7 giving information **d)** 1 giving an opinion & 5 describing a character **e)** 4 creating suspense
f) 2 giving advice
3 **a)** understand how awful he felt
b) exaggeration, comparison
c) show that things get better
d) entertain

4 **a)** inform, amuse, persuade
b) *inform*: I sobbed myself to sleep last night. I feel awful, I hate it here. I had a weird Spanish fishy thing; *amuse*: Pie Ella or something … Or get a job; *persuade*: Can't I come home? Please let me come home.
Check with your teacher if you think you have found another correct one.

Test yourself: practice reading tests

Reading test 1: Love Affairs

Page 31: Text A

1 **a)** Manchester United
b) European Cup Final
2 Your answer should include three aspects: the writer is a big fan of the player and has been for a long time; he feels a special relationship with him.
3 **a)** shows tension **b)** shows excitement **c)** shows tension **d)** shows excitement **e)** shows excitement
4 **a)** False **b)** False **c)** True **d)** True **e)** False
5 **a)** 3 **b)** 2 **c)** 4 **d)** 1

Page 33: Text B

6 groaned
7 **a)** share ice cream **b)** write letters to each other
8 H+C: Biology, Textiles, Home Science, Assembly, rollcall; N+F: Chemistry, Computers
9 They are spoken with emphasis/they are stressed.
10 Wants to please Fleur/not lose her: OK, I'll write you a letter; unromantic: lick of my ice cream; Thinks he understands girls: that's a bad sign
Ask your teacher if you have found others.

Reading test 2: Emergency!

Page 34: Text A

slowly; heavily
he realises they could be in a lot of trouble
taking to his heels
emphasises it, makes it sound stronger
spilled drink; pretending to be hurt
a) Dan **b)** People in the room/Dan **c)** Dan **d)** skinhead

Page 37: Text B

1 **e)** sit the patient down
2 **c)** cover the wound
3 **d)** put your hand over it
4 **b)** squeeze tight
5 **a)** raise the arm or leg
wrong address; animals; getting cut off
because it is a list of things that happen; it is in the order they happen.
10 ordinary people (explanation to include: content would be known to a doctor – not to an ordinary person; language/words used – simple not medical).

Writing skills

ages 40–41: Using a wider variety of connectives

a) because **b)** but **c)** and **d)** because **e)** but **f)** but **g)** because **h)** and
a) but **b)** and **c)** because **d)** and **e)** but **f)** but **g)** because **h)** and
a) so **b)** then **c)** or **d)** or **e)** but **f)** because **g)** but **h)** or **i)** so **j)** but
Ask your teacher to check your answers.

Pages 42–43: Adding detail by using adjectives

1 *Check answers with your teacher.*
2 **a)** brand-new, top-quality **b)** coloured **c)** useful, brand-new **d)** top-quality, brand-new **e)** real, top-quality, coloured
3 *Check answers with your teacher.*
4 **a)** battered **b)** teenage **c)** e.g. awful, grim, run-down **d)** e.g. hopeless, young, grubby **e** e.g. dirty, cramped, dark **f)** e.g. broken, wobbly, unsafe
5 **a)** smashed, broken, cracked **b)** top-class, excellent **c)** messy **d)** broken, smashed **e)** cracked, broken **f)** rusty **g)** crumpled **h)** small

Pages 44–45: Using adverbs to help a reader

1 **a)** firstly **b)** exactly **c)** safely, tightly **d)** soon **e)** approximately **f)** Luckily **g)** safely **h)** finally
2 **a)** patiently (how) **b)** suddenly (when) **c)** noisily (how) **d)** angrily (how) **e)** First (when), carefully (how) **f)** next (when), gently (how) **g)** furiously (how) **h)** loudly (how)
3 *Check with your teacher.*
4 *Check with your teacher.*

Pages 46–47: Using full stops and capital letters to mark sentences

1 **a)** Remember to buy dog food. Dad wants his dinner early tonight. **b)** Can you get the hedge trimmer sharpened? The hairdresser rang to cancel your appointment. **c)** The hamster has escaped again. We must get the front door lock changed. **d)** The car's got a leak. Please buy more toilet rolls.
2 **a)** … go exploring. She made …
b) … very lazy. She sat … the roadside. A couple of …
c) … behind her. It sounded … dustbin lid. She turned … watching her. They did not …
d) … felt uncomfortable. What were the … girls up to? She decided … way home. The group … watch her. Amina didn't … into a shop. She did not fancy …
3 **a)** The leader of the gang seemed to be the small girl in the black T-shirt. She was chewing gum and carrying a large shiny red handbag.
b) The other small one was obviously her sister because their faces were so alike. Both had dark brown eyes and dead straight hair.
c) Would they give her any trouble? Amina smiled nervously and moved past them back towards the alleyway and home. She hoped they wouldn't follow her.
d) Her heart pounded. She decided to do nothing but she would ask her cousin about them later on. She had been silly to go out alone on her first day. She realised this now.
4 **a)** Chile's, Spider Girls, Santiago, January, August, Dior, Chanel, Armani
b) gangs / they; Santiago / their; chance / they; climb up / the next; is easy / they just; Armani / why did; do it / because they

Pages 48–49: Improving the organisation of ideas

1 **a)** i **b)** iv **c)** ii
2 *Sample answers:*
a) Mobile phones are a good way of communicating. **b)** Riding a bike is a good choice of transport.
3 *Ask your teacher to mark this task.*
4 **There is one way it could improve and that is by getting some new stars to be the judges**. You need younger and more famous stars to get people to watch it. //
It needs to be on at a different time. It starts when people are still busy. A lot of people are trying to get home from work or school then. Starting two hours later would be better. //
I hope you make those changes. If you don't, I think the programme will fail.

Pages 50–51: Developing an idea

1 **a) times:** times of the day
food: where canteen is, what the food is like
what to do if you get lost: times of the day, where the office is, people you can ask for help, what the staff are like, information on noticeboards
b) times of the day
2: **a)** 2 **b)** 4 or 5 **c)** 4 or 5
3: *Ask your teacher to check your answers.*

Pages 52–53: Writing for a reader

1 *The answers here are for guidance only. There is no right or wrong answer.*
Parents: a, b, c, e, f, h, i
Best friend: b, c, e, f, g
Teacher: c
2a) & 2b) All the sentences are about Dave rather than the food itself.
3 **1** C **2** E **3** A **4** D
4 *Ask your teacher to check your answers.*

Pages 54–55: Using interesting words for effect

1 Any ideas will be correct. The important thing is to have the ideas.
2 Four ideas is good. Six ideas is excellent.
3 Any words could be correct. The important thing is to think about word choices.

Pages 56–57: Choose an appropriate form and style

1 **a) i)** I **ii)** F **iii)** F **iv)** I **v)** I **vi)** I/F **vii)** I **viii)** F **ix)** F **x)** F
1 **b) i)** True **ii)** False **iii)** False
1 **c)** Do not use abbreviations, e.g. I'm, He's.; Avoid common words, e.g. want, ask.; Use longer, complex sentences.
2 Answers will vary but examples as follows:
a) My father thinks that computer games are a waste of time.
b) I look forward to seeing you next week.
c) If you would like to, you are welcome to visit tomorrow.
3 Answers will vary but examples as follows:
a) (Friend's name) is really great. He's always good for a chat and never drops you in it.
b) (Friend's name) is a model student. He is always punctual and works well with a variety of people.

Page 58: How to tackle the writing task

If you have given more detail than this, so much the better. The important thing is that you have thought about the differences between different types of writing.

	Who is the writer?	Who is the reader?	What is the form?	What is the purpose?
A	business woman	Bank manager, an experienced profesional in money matters.	formal letter	To give information about the project/to persuade the manager to lend money
B	teenage boy	Best friend, probably teenage boy.	email	To describe/give information about a festival/to review bands or songs/to entertain or amuse a friend
C	journalist	People, male and female, of all ages around the country	newspaper report	To give factual information about the event/to hold the reader's interest
D	novelist	Readers of all ages, male and female.	novel	To entertain readers/to use imagination and invent/to make readers feel part of an imagined situation/to describe places, events or people

Test yourself: practice writing tasks

Page 59: Longer writing task

Check your answers with your teacher.

Page 59: Shorter writing task

Check your answers with your teacher.